THE CORONADOS ISLANDS

Their History and Environment

General Coordinator:
Virgilio Muñoz

Editorial Committee:
José Luis Castro Ruiz
Carlos De Alba Pérez
Rubén Lara Lara
Jorge Martínez Zepeda
Roberto Millán Núñez
Virgilio Muñoz

Design:
Medicis Communication

Art:
Josué Ríos G./Jorge Valdivia J.

Photography Coordinator:
Alfonso Caraveo Castro

Printing Coordinator:
Rodolfo Pataky

English Version Translators:
Marina Dillingham
Enrique Nava López

The Coronados Islands, Their History and Environment
First Edition 2007.

Their History and Environment

THE CORONADOS ISLANDS

Their History and Environment

Chevron

PREFACE

For Chevron, it is of great importance and value to launch research projects like the one we are submitting today. The book The Coronados Islands, Their History and Environment, explores in depth, the many facets of the history and environment of these impressive islands.

The Chevron Corporation is committed to the economic and social development of the areas surrounding its work-sites. Historically, Chevron has earned the reputation of being the ideal community partner because it holds in high priority the need to observe and respect a community's way of life. Through its actions, Chevron seeks a sense of identity and belonging within the communities in which they are so heavily invested.

Our actions, based on The Chevron Way, allow us to establish successful, long-lasting alliances, which help us develop sustainable projects as part of one of our central goals: the care and preservation of natural resources and the environment. This is the foundation of our global wealth, and a legacy that will be treasured by future generations.

A modern and responsible vision of ecology does not oppose human development and progress. Our challenge is to combine our determination for growth and advancement with the ethical need to contribute to the care and preservation of the environment, the flora and fauna, the planet's enormous biodiversity and the balance of its multiple ecosystems.

By supporting research projects such as the one presented here, Chevron emphasizes its unyielding commitment to the free expression of ideas and the progress of science in all fields of knowledge. Chevron will continue to support the serious and responsible academic work of researchers who strive to enlighten us and enrich our lives by revealing the secrets of our surroundings.

CARLOS ATALLAH
PRESIDENT OF CHEVRON DE BAJA CALIFORNIA

INTRODUCTION

The Coronados Islands are a subtle part of our coastal landscape. Their existence is taken for granted and we frequently overlook them, allowing them to escape our notice and gradually vanish into a thick mist of habit and routine. Every now and then the islands resurface out of the mist, to reappear as scattered references in a story, an anecdote, or a fisherman's tale.

To know the islands, to feel them and to recover the lost memories belonging to this part of our territory is the vision that inspired the group of researchers that came together to write this book. Knowledge clears the mist and ushers in true appreciation.

The authors' goal is to offer all Baja Californians a collection of facts and information so they can form an accurate and thorough profile of the region and the islands in particular.

The Coronados Islands, Their History and Environment is divided into five sections: Histories and Protagonists, Fishing Activities, the Physical Environment, the Islands and Their Habitat, and the Marine Environment. Each theme and subject will immerse the reader in the intricacies of the Coronados Islands.

This book will provide intriguing information about the islands, ranging from the maritime expeditions of the 16th century and the Sunday excursions of the 19th century, to a retrospective analysis of the legal framework governing the islands. The reader will discover facts about the legendary hotel/casino that operated on the islands during prohibition. This book will provide information about diving, boats and fishing in the area through the stories of coastal fishermen whose lives revolve around the ocean swells.

Readers will also learn about sustainability (habitat conditions that affect the production of marine food), species reproduction and floating cages for tuna fattening. The authors describe the islands' ecosystems and their potential as well as the spectacular displays of flora and fauna, land creatures, sea mammals and birds that inhabit the islands. After reading this book, one will understand that these are an essential part of the islands' unique scenery.

Environmental topics such as the age of the islands, their geological makeup, issues relating to ecological breakdown and the role and study of marine currents and tides will be approached. These issues are of great concern because the sea is often the final destination of many pollutants.

Chevron's participation has been an invaluable component in the development of this work. Their patronage made it possible to create a single manuscript incorporating both the results of the scientific research promoted by Chevron over the last few years and many worthy facts which previously lay scattered in a variety of scientific and journalistic archives throughout the region.

The Coronados Islands, Their History and Environment is a valuable contribution to our knowledge of this landmark because it focuses our sight on those familiar islands ever present on our horizon.

VIRGILIO MUÑOZ

THE CORONADOS ISLANDS

Content

THE CORONADOS ISLANDS

CHAPTER I

HISTORIES AND PROTAGONISTS
THE CORONADOS ISLANDS

Tourism and Commerce 1870-1958

LAWRENCE DOUGLAS TAYLOR HANSEN*

During the last few decades of the 19th century, Mexican and foreign investors set their sights on the Coronados Islands and their natural resources. As they explored the islands, the area became exposed to other opportunities such as the tourism industry.

Beginnings of Tourism and Commerce

The tourism business centered on the Coronados Islands began in the early 1870s, when a San Diego captain named Samuel Sumner Dunnells began running Sunday excursions aboard steam boats departing from San Diego. These excursions remained in operation throughout the 1880s. Groups of people also began to make one or two-day fishing and camping trips to the islands. These trips were unauthorized entrances into Mexican territory since neither the operators of the excursions or the independent parties visiting the islands requested permission from the Mexican government before heading for the islands.[1]

During this period, San Diego fishermen began fishing commercially in the waters around the islands. In February 1869, two San Diego companies (Davis and Purdy) built some huts on the archipelago. In 1873, groups of Chinese fishermen departing from San Diego in Chinese junks, exploited abalone and shark in the waters surrounding the islands. The abalone shells were sent to workshops in San Diego and other cities to make jewelry.[2]

Several enterprises were organized with the purpose of mining the abundant sandstone found on North Coronados Island. Retired Colonel Manuel A. Ferrer (of San Diego) and Tore Fidel Pujol (editor of the Baja California newspaper in La Paz) led the first group of mining investors. The company formed by Ferrer and Pujol began its operations around the middle of the 1880s and successfully exported tons of stone to the United States.[3] Later, Ferrer's mining grant was transferred to the Hanbury and Garvey Corporation and subsequently to Haines

*Professor-researcher at the Department of Cultural Studies of El Colegio de la Frontera Norte. He has a doctorate in Latin America History at El Colegio de México. His areas of interest in research refer to the history of the border region between México and the United States as well as the trans-border cultural relations. His most recent book is El Nuevo Norteamericano: la Integración Continental y su Impacto Sobre la Cultura y la Identidad Nacional en la Época del TLCAN (México: CISAN/Colef, 2001).

©San Diego Historical Society

and Connors of San Francisco. The mining of stone in the islands continued until the middle of the 1890s, when it ceased with the development of other quarries in San Diego and Southern California.

In 1897, the Mexican government began requiring that tourism agencies obtain written authorization through the Mexican Consulate in San Diego before setting off to the islands. The official in charge at the time was Colonel Agustín Sanginés, military commander and political head of the Baja California Northern District. At Sanginés' request, the steamboat "Carlos Pacheco" of the Lower California Development Company was commissioned to call on the islands to monitor tourist and visitor activity.

However, without permanent personnel on the island, it was impossible for the government to adequately supervise the area.[5] Some visitors included migrant workers who sought entrance into the United States. In 1911, eleven Chinese citizens were abandoned by smugglers on North Coronados Island, where they starved to death.

Tourism was interrupted between 1911 and 1915 due to the activities of Mexican rebel groups along the California border. In 1916, the Star and Crescent Boat Company resumed excursions by offering trips on glass-bottom boats that departed several times a week from the dock at the base of Broadway in San Diego, California. The company continued offering these trips during a period of great tourist activity that eventually ended in the mid 1930s, when the company closed its operations.[6]

THE CORONADOS ISLANDS

During Prohibition (1919-1933), the islands were used to smuggle liquor into the United States. According to Francisco Regalado (a former smuggler from Ensenada), smugglers who participated in liquor transportation earned up to $300 a day. According to Regalado, smugglers brought the liquor from Canada and unloaded it in Bajo San José, approximately 30 miles south of Ensenada. From that point, the liquor was transported along the coast to various California ports.

The Coronados Islands were the transfer point between the freight ships and the speed boats that made the final and most dangerous leg of the trip to San Diego. Once in San Diego, the merchandise was transferred to other vessels that were headed north to Los Angeles and other major cities. Bootleggers could seek temporary refuge in Puerto Cueva or "Smugglers Cove," an inlet located on the northeastern side of South Coronados Island.[7]

The Coronado Islands Yacht Club

In August 1932, Mexican investors Mariano Escobedo González and Manuel Metions obtained a concession from the Mexican government to build a hotel/casino in Puerto Cueva. Fred G. Hamilton, former manager of the Benson Lumber Company of California, was an important partner within the group of investors.[8] The hotel, called Coronado Islands Yacht Club, was built on wood piles on the Puerto Cueva Bay. This was the best anchoring ground in the archipelago. The facilities consisted of 60 rooms, a few bungalows, a restaurant, a cabaret and a casino.

Just like the Agua Caliente Casino, the interiors were magnificent, with wall-to-wall carpeting and huge mirrors on the walls. The focal point of the

©San Diego Historical Society

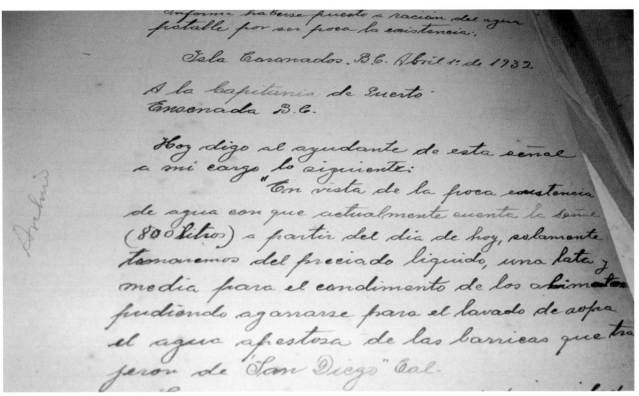

Ligthhouse log regarding limited water supply on the islands.

cabaret was a beautifully polished wooden bar. Above the second floor was a large balcony from which the guests could enjoy a panoramic view of the coast, from Rosarito to San Diego's Point Loma. The amenities included a double-decker fishing boat and a glass-bottom boat for the guests' enjoyment of the marine life present on and around the islands. After all of the construction work was finished, the total cost reached approximately $200,000 which was a considerable sum at the time.

Despite the large investment, the hotel did not do well. One major setback was that all materials and supplies had to be transported from the mainland by boat. When Prohibition was abolished on December 5, 1933, the hotel lost one of its main attractions for US tourists. Within a very short time the hotel was practically deserted. The final blow came early in January 1935, when President Cardenas ordered that all the casinos in the country be shut down. Despite the decree, the yacht club owners planned to reopen the hotel on May 25, 1935, offering live performances, food and drinks at mainland prices. However, their efforts failed and both the building and its adjacent area became Mexican state property.[10]

The End of the Tourism Era

In 1954, the federal government created a law forbidding tourists from landing on the islands. This law aimed to prevent further destruction of the flora and fauna, as well as to strengthen the efforts initiated in 1924, when the government (under the advice of Professor José Martín Gallegos of the National Museum of México City) designated the islands as a sea bird refuge.[11]

In 1958, the Star and Crescent Company once again began offering excursions to the archipelago, but the company did not allow the passengers to disembark on the islands. It appears that the excursions ended shortly thereafter because there is no available data relating to their operation after that date.[12] Since then, the only excursions originating in San Diego have been organized by the San Diego Natural History Museum and a few other institutions. The museum has been offering annual excursions to its members since the 1930s even though the passengers are no longer permitted to disembark from their boats to step foot on the islands' soils. Scientists interested in visiting the islands for research must now request permission to do so with the Ensenada naval authorities.[13]

It is unlikely that the Coronados Islands will ever offer on-site facilities for tourists again. Preventing the general public's access to the archipelago is considered the only effective way to protect the natural environment and its ecosystem. Nevertheless, it is now possible to promote boat excursions that allow the public to enjoy the beauty and majesty of the islands and surrounding areas from a distance. These laws and regulations have been established to protect the islands' ecology.

Works Cited

1. San Diego Union, May 12, October 6, 1870, June 5-6, 1873, February 2, 1881.
2. San Diego Union, October 6, 1870; Robert A. Nash, "The Chinese Fishing Industry in Baja California," Baja California Symposium IX, Santa Ana, California, May 1971, pp. 4, 9-10.
3. San Diego Union, May 23, November 17, 1872; January 26, May 10, July 11,1873; October 18, 1881; February 1, November 16, 1882.
4. Articles of Incorporation, Coronado Islands Company, en San Diego Historical Society, Archive: Companies: Articles of Incorporation, Files 415 and 568; San Diego Union, April 4, 1888; April 28, 1893.
5. Coronel Sanguinés to the Secretario de Gobernación, January 17, 1898 and Secretario de Gobernación to Sanguinés, February 10, 1898, in Archivo General de la Nación (AGN), Archives: Gobernación, Ref.: Volume 360, Section 2a. File 13, Instituto de Investigaciones Históricas, Universidad Autónoma de Baja California (IIH-UABC), Box 32, File 34.
6. San Diego Railroad Museum, Report 13-4, San Diego Union, May 21,1958.
7. Interview with Francisco Regalado, by Martha Edna Castillo, October 4, 1996, Archivo de la Palabra, IIH-UABC, No. PHO-E/1(1); Helen Ellsberg, Los Coronados Islands (Glendale, Cal.: La Siesta Press, 1970), p. 11.

8. Contract No. 127, between Manuel Escobedo and the Secretaría de Agricultura y Fomento, August 15, 1932, and contract with Mariano Escobedo, to rent the federal zone of the archipelago Coronados, B.C., December 4, 1933, AGN: Archives of the Secretaría de Comunicaciones y Obras Públicas, Ref.: Vol. 534, File 128, IIH-UABC, Box 18, File 8.
9. San Diego Union, June 10, 1932.
10. San Diego Union, May 5, 24; July 22-23, 1935.
11. San Diego Union, April 20, 1924; Carlos R. Berzunza, "Las Islas Coronados y San Benito," Archive of the Boletín de la Sociedad Mexicana de Geografía y Estadística, Ref.: Vol. LXXIX, No. 3, May 1955, June 1955, IIH-UABC, Box 2, File 20, pp. 382-383.
12. San Diego Union, May 21, 1958.
13. San Diego Union, May 28, 1934, Section 2, p. 1,June 12, 1940, June 5, 1949; San Diego Evening Tribune, May 24, 1976.

THE LAWS OF THE CORONADOS ISLANDS: A HISTORICAL PERSPECTIVE

VIRGILIO MUÑOZ*

Baja Californians know little about the Coronados Islands. All they possess are bits of information gleaned from the scattered tales of adventures passed on by local fishermen and foreign settlers. These accounts are sparse, often inaccurate and limited to incidental anecdotes that remind us about the islands' sovereignty.

There is a vast record of facts and circumstances that catalog the Mexicans' detached relationship with the islands and the sea around them. Several important events have shaped the legal and political status of the islands: the Guadalupe-Hidalgo treaty, the 19th century constitutions, the Constitution of 1917 and other federal, state and municipal laws.

The Guadalupe-Hidalgo Treaty

The Guadalupe-Hidalgo Treaty formally ended the war between México and the United States on February 2, 1848. It conceded the territories of Alta California, Texas and New Mexico to the United States. The treaty made no reference to the Coronados Islands (located seven miles south of the international border) as part of the northern limits of México's national territory.[1]

The omission may be due to the fact that the commissions formed by both countries to discuss the terms of the Treaty for Peace, Friendship and Borders were involved in a dispute over Washington D.C.'s proposal to obtain authorization for the free transit of American troops through the Isthmus of Tehuantepec.[2] This dispute would define the destiny of the areas currently known as Baja California, Northern Tamaulipas, Coahuila, Chihuahua and Sonora.

*An attorney who graduated from the National Autonomous University of México, also holds a master in education from the Universidad Iberoamericana. He has been a university professor and has co-authored history and civics textbooks as well as works on education, law and politics. He was director-founder of the Diario 29 newspaper, secretary of education for the state of Baja California and a featured writer and commentator in the written press and on television. He is currently a consultant for public and private agencies, and director of the Foro Esta Región.

According to United States Congressional Representative Nicholas P. Trist, American interests were centered on the "conquest" of uninhabited lands.[3] They aimed to extend their dominion over areas where the population was scarce in order to alleviate the demographic pressure the United States was experiencing at the time.

To give an idea of the population density in the region at that time, the towns of San Diego, Monterrey and San Francisco in Alta California had a little over one thousand inhabitants. San Antonio Bejar in Texas had a population of two thousand. The total population of Mexico was just under six million and was mostly concentrated in the center of the territory.[4]

The population that settled south of the Rio Bravo (Grande) presented a problem to North Americans. This fact weighed heavily on the spirit of their demands and proposed border limits. The settlers proved to be a threat, a source of conflict, and a factor of destabilization in the region.

Insular Territory Standards

Mexico's Constitución Política delineates and establishes the extent of the Mexican territory. Several constitutions have governed Mexico throughout the years. They include the Spanish Constitution of 1812, the Federalist Constitution of 1824, the Laws of 1836 and 1857 and the current Constitution of 1917. They generally state that the islands found on the "adjacent seas" or "adjacent in both seas" are part of the national territory. This is all that establishes the Coronados Islands' subjugation to the sovereignty of Mexico and to its laws.

The current constitution also declares that the national territory includes the islands in adjacent seas according to the terms set forth by international law. It also illustrates that "the states of the Federation shall maintain the areas and limits which they have had thus far." This suggests that the limits of the federative entities and those of the islands are specified in the body of some previous constitution.

In order to identify the origin of those statements, it is necessary to go back to the Constitution of 1824. This constitution states that constitutional law "shall delineate the federation borders as soon as circumstances allow."[5] Such delineation was never issued. This loophole in the law is therefore addressed by the issue of historical possession of national territory and the reiterated statement of acts of authority or sovereignty which comprise the islands.

Local Jurisdiction

Only a few federal entities have constitutions that specify that the islands in close proximity to them are under their jurisdiction. Baja California's constitution does not specifically identify its territory. It states that "the portion of national territory that corresponds to the State is that which has been recognized by the Political Constitution of the Mexican United States."

Article 8 of the Municipal Organic Law (which determines the abilities of municipalities with regards to local laws) defines the territorial limits of each municipality. It states that the "Coronado Island" forms part of the Tijuana Township. It refers to the islands singularly as Coronado.

It is possible that its legislature did not include the islands in the text because of the logic set forth by article 48 of the Magna Carta which states, "The islands…of adjacent seas pertaining to national

territory…shall directly depend on the Government of the Federation, except for the islands over which the States have exercised jurisdiction until now."

Baja California was considered federal territory until 1953, when it became the 29th state to be incorporated to the federal pact. Consequently, the adjacent islands have been under federal jurisdiction.

This discussion was not intended to resolve whether the islands are under federal or municipal jurisdiction. The use of the Organic Law can be justified as a practical means to an end. Organic Law is used by municipalities and states to justify their potential interests in the islands.[6] The law identifies the appropriate authority on municipal matters in a territory under federal jurisdiction.

To illustrate the municipal and state interests in the islands, politicians have made visits to the islands. Mayor Federico Valdez Martínez visited the islands on November 18, 1987. Prior to that, another Tijuana mayor, Mr. Marco Antonio Bolaños Cacho led a visit. These visits were conducted in accordance with all applicable legal requirements and with the prior consent and support of the Department of the Navy. This means that the municipal authorities were recognized by the federal entities.

The insular territory is not exempt from eventually coming under private ownership. Currently Mexico has about 75 privately owned islands.[7] In accordance with the first paragraph of article 27 of the constitution, "Ownership of lands and waters within the borders of the national territory is the right of the Nation, which in turn has the right to transfer dominion to third parties, thus placing the land under private ownership."

Other Legislation

The question of who governs the islands leads us to a body of laws that deal with topics such as national sovereignty, federal administration of public domain, territory under national jurisdiction, the responsibility of public agencies to the administration and protection and supervision of insular territory.[8]

Despite all the political and economic importance of its islands and their scientific and historical value, Mexico has no general law regarding this insular territory. It has a regulation "that better defines the agencies corresponding to the different levels of government, public domain, private property and legally documents the islands' location, dimensions, resources, as well as their incorporation to the rest of the national economy."[9]

In the case of the Coronados Islands, it is important to consider the terms of the Organic Law of the Federal Public Administration. This law states that it is the responsibility of the Secretaría de Gobernación (Department of the Interior) to "manage the islands under federal jurisdiction." This task is generally carried out through the Subdirección del Territorio Insular (Administration of Insular

Territory) unless the administration of a particular territory corresponds by law to another agency or entity of the federal government.

There are several agencies present on the Coronados Islands. Among them is a detachment of the Secretaría de Marina (Department of the Navy) which is charged with safeguarding and supervising the islands. The Capitanía de Puerto (Harbor Master) is a part of the Department of Communications and Transportation and is in charge of maritime signaling tasks. CICESE (Centro de Investigacion Cientifica y Educacion Superior de Ensenada) and UABC (Universidad Autónoma de Baja California) have installed monitoring devices that measure rainfall, winds, earthquakes and ocean currents. The SCT and the Comisión Federal de Electricidad (Federal Commission of Electricity) have equipped the islands with telephone and radio repeaters.

The legal framework that governs the islands reveals some of the islands' more interesting facets and contributes to the knowledge and appreciation of this territory. As stated by professor Miguel González Avelar, "the islands are not disposable fragments of the state, or particles of sovereignty scattered over the waters, but an integral part of the national territory."[10]

Works Cited
1. Treaty of Guadalupe-Hidalgo, February 2, 1848, between México and the United States, with the amendments of the US Senate and approved by the Mexican Government.
2. Musacchio, Humberto. Milenios de México, Vol. III, Diccionario Enciclopédico de México, México, 1999, pp. 3070-3072.
3. Ibíd. pp. 3071
4. Vázquez, Josefina Zoraida, Una Historia de México, Vol. II. Editorial Patria, México, 1994, p. 271.
5. Tena Ramírez, Felipe, Derecho Constitucional Mexicano, Editorial Porrúa, México, 1967, p. 186.
6. Salgado Pérez, Rodolfo, Consideraciones Jurídicas en Torno de las Islas Coronados (Notes)
7. Initiative of Ley General del Territorio Insular de la Nación, presented for the Diputado Federal Amador Rodríguez Lozano, April 22, 2003.
8. Ley Federal del Mar (Articles 3, 15, 23, 34, 57-65); Ley General de Bienes Nacionales (Article 6, I y III); Ley de Navegación (Article 6); Ley Orgánica de la Administración Pública Federal (Article 27, XI, 30, IV, XI); Reglamento Interior de la Secretaría de Gobernación (Article 12, X); Ley Orgánica de la Armada de México (Article 2)
9. Interview with Amador Rodríguez Lozano
10. González Avelar, Miguel, Clipperton, Isla Mexicana, Editorial Fondo de Cultura Económica, México, 1992, p. 17.

THE CORONADOS ISLANDS

Ensenada, B.C.

SAILORS ON LAND,
TESTIMONIES OF RIPARIAN FISHERMEN

VÍCTOR ALEJANDRO ESPINOZA VALLE*

The riparian fishermen of Baja California treasure and cherish the sea, due to the fact that it is central to their existence. They respect it, love it and depend on it. These people strive to prosper from the wealth of the ocean.

Most riparian fishermen had their fishing tradition passed to them from their past relatives in Baja California. They woke every morning with a majestic view of the Coronados Islands and learned to walk on the sand and play with pebbles from the beach.

*Researcher at El Colegio de la Frontera Norte and a national researcher for the Sistema Nacional de Investigadores. His latest works are El Voto Lejano. Cultura Política y Migración México-Estados Unidos, 2004. He is co-coordinator of the book Después de la Alternancia: Elecciones y Nueva Competitividad, 2005.

The Call of the Sea

Alfonso Cortés López

I was born January 3, 1937 in Tijuana, Baja California. My family came from La Paz, in Southern Baja California. My entire family has been fishermen: my grandparents, uncles and parents.

The first time I went to the Coronados Islands was in 1949. I left from Ensenada in a small, low boat called a G22 Coastguard. We made the trip at night, very slowly. My uncle, a navy captain who worked on that boat, took me to the islands. I remember the two-story hotel that stood there. It was very pretty. It had all the main services and facilities, like beds and tables. All we had to bring was a stove, pots and food. The fishermen stayed in the lower level and the soldiers used the top floor. The navy was not there

yet, as they did not take charge until 1952 or 1953. The kitchen and casino were on the lower level. The cellar was accessed by a staircase that also went up to the roof, where other fishermen lived.

There is a very narrow rock near the rear part of the island. The only things there were water tanks. There also used to be goats, but they were eradicated because they ate the vegetation. The island is practically bare, but you can find quail, birds and sparrows there. We fishermen have given every part of the island a name, like "Las Muelas," "La Puerta" or "La Cueva del Chivo." I had a small room on the island where I could stay when I needed to. I am the only fisherman who had one.

You Have to Protect What is Yours

As a child, I went to school at Justo Sierra Elementary School in Ensenada. It was in Ensenada where my family had our house and a very large plot of land that we owned with my uncles. I came to this area only during the summer to fish with my father. After visiting the islands in 1949, I decided to become a fisherman. I told myself that "I better go to the Coronados Islands."

I put up with school until the fourth grade, and by 1950 I was already helping the fishermen. When I was twelve, I began work at the Ensenada cooperative. At the time, the cooperative's chairman was Alfonso Reynoso, who was a neighbor and a good friend of the family. He had a lobster boiling facility in the Independencia neighborhood. He was elderly and very helpful to all fishermen.

One day Alfonso said to me: "you want to be a fisherman, but you don't want to study any longer." I replied that I would rather be a fisherman and that I wanted to join the cooperative. I wanted to be a member in order to have a co-op ID. Having a co-op ID was not the same as having a fourth grade school ID. He agreed to send me out to sea the next lobster season with an older co-op member, on a two-year trial basis. I had to say I was 21 years old for purposes of insurance. It was okay because Alfonso arranged everything.

Ensenada was a very small town then and everybody knew everybody. Local authorities (like the mayor), had lots of contact with the fishermen and they were on very good terms. By 1955, I had set up my camp, bought a panga boat, an engine and wooden traps. Today I am chairman of the board of the El Morro Riparian Fishermen's Union.

The El Morro area was originally called Playas de Cortés between kilometer 36 to 40. When fishermen (like my grandfather and uncles) would pass in their trucks, they would be asked: "Where are you going?" They would reply, "To el morrito." El Morro got the name because it is a little stone mound on Playas de Cortes.

Carlos León Pino

I was born in Tijuana in 1946. My mother was from Sonora, and my father was from Southern Baja California. He was born on a ranch across from Ciudad Constitución, which is part of Sierra La Giganta. My mother moved to Loreto to work there, but she did not enjoy keeping cattle in the desert. Both of my grandfathers were fishermen.

My father began fishing near La Bufadora in Punta Banda, where he met my mother. When they got married they came to live in El Morro. The family consisted of six: two sisters, two brothers and my parents. We went to Abraham Lincoln Elementary School in Rosarito and attended night school at Miguel F. Martínez High School in Tijuana.

My brother Jorge and I are both fishermen. I began fishing when I was 12 or 13. Sure, I went to school, but I went there in my spare time. I was attracted by the water. We devoted ourselves to fishing because there was nothing else to do.

We are riparian fishermen because we fish in the shallow part of the ocean up to 10 miles offshore. Beyond that, the bottom is too deep and other kinds of vessels and fishing equipment are required. We have belonged to the Baja California Riparian Fishermen's Union since it was established in 1989. We have a permit that allows us to fish around the islands up to Punta Azul. Unfortunately, the catch is becoming scarce; many fishermen have arrived from other parts and have no respect for the law. When my father was alive, there was plenty of fish for everybody. There were very few fishermen and they cared about the species they sought. They would not fish them to extinction.

We caught lobster during lobster season, from September 15 to February 15. The other months of the year we concentrated on scale fish and sea urchin. We exported the sea urchin to Japan, as there is no market for it in Mexico. There is a small market for it in California, but virtually all the sea urchin goes to

Japan after being processed in Ensenada plants.

When I first went to the Coronados Islands, the hotel that allegedly belonged to Al Capone was still standing. The authorities allowed us to come and stay at the hotel during lobster season. Each of us took a small room during the week, returned home over the weekend to deliver the product and then went back to the islands.

We left with my father from Campo López in boats with no motors. We had to row. We took food for the marines and lighthouse keepers, who had children and grandchildren around our own age. My father used to pick up the lighthouse keeper's kids after school and take them back home. During the holidays my father also picked up the lighthouse keeper's wife and children.

We still have a good relationship with the keeper. Sometimes he calls us and asks us to bring him something. My brother Jorge stays in his house during lobster season, which is a tradition from my father's times. I have to stay behind and tend the family restaurant, but Jorge prefers being there. He lived on the island for 18 years and virtually never left it. Occasionally he came to land on weekends, but he returned to the island early Monday mornings.

The point of departure for the island has always been Popotla, because its port offers protection against groundswells. In summertime when the sea is calmer, we leave from El Morro because we have a panga boat there.

Only the Sea Knows

Manuel Medina Villavicencio

I was born in Ensenada, Baja California on November 23, 1954. My grandparents arrived by ship from Santa Rosalíta. My father was also born in Ensenada. We moved from the Guerrero neighborhood of Ensenada to Bahía de los Ángeles, back to Ensenada and eventually we settled in El Morro.

My love for the sea began in my childhood, like my own children, who already work by my side. Like most of the other fishermen's children, I went to primary school, high school and crafts school in Rosarito; but the sea was my life. Even so, the sea has not been kind to me. I had three accidents in 1982 and almost drowned. I stopped fishing between 1984 and 1985 and thought about leaving for the U.S. But no matter what I tried, the beach or the hills, I was never able to cross, so I went to work on a ranch. Later some friends asked me if I knew how to fish, so I decided to get back to the trade. I became confident again and got a little panga boat in 1987. I am now chairman of the Baja California Riparian Fishermen Union, one of the six fishermen's unions established in the area.

The first time I went to the Coronados Islands I was 14 years old. One of my uncles told me that if I was not going to go to school any longer, then I should go to the islands to help them. I remember the fog was very thick. Someone said to me, "When we get to the island, we will go to the high part where there are large oranges and even apples." He lied. The first time you go there, you get desperate because it feels like the trip will never end. We had been traveling for two hours and the island still felt nowhere near. When we finally arrived, the island was bare. There was nothing.

I was with abalone divers. When we landed, they prepared all their gear and went diving, but my uncle told me to fix the food.

I had never cooked before. There was a tin of beef, but I did not know how to prepare it. I found a can of peas and another of mixed vegetables, so I threw in a bunch of things, everything I could find. Afterwards, one of the divers came out of the water and told me he was very hungry and asked if I had fixed anything to eat. He ate my food and really liked it.

Unfortunately, the islands' abalone supply has been exhausted because of excess take. Abalone grows very slowly and if not allowed to develop properly, it does not reproduce. The weather can also influence the development of certain species. For example, cold winter water is not good for lobster, but it is great for sea urchin. During the last "El Niño," the water was hot and there was plenty of lobster, but the sea urchin was not good. I remember cutting open a sea urchin, and the meat would fall apart. Once, the abundance of lobster in Puerto Nuevo created a new tradition for cooking lobster. Since the fishermen had nothing else to eat, they would cut open the lobster and dump it into hot oil. We've been eating it like that for about 50 years.

We are riparian fishermen, like our fathers and brothers before us. We belong to this shore, just like our children and grandchildren. The sea has secrets which it keeps for itself, but every day it tells us what it feels. Every day we go fishing, the islands rise in front of us. We love them and respect them. The sea is our home, and so are the Coronados Islands.

Always sailors on land, like Rafael Alberti wanted.

LAND AND SEA EXPLORATIONS

JORGE MARTÍNEZ ZEPEDA*

Discovery

Fray Juan De Torquemada 1614.

From the time the Spanish arrived in the Baja California peninsula in 1535, a series of expeditions were conducted with the purpose of surveying the coastline and discovering its economic potential. The expeditions identified resources such as fish, lobster, abalone, pearls, mining, salt mines and guano. [a]

The northern part of the peninsula was "discovered" after a journey made by Francisco de Ulloa in 1539. Another expedition led by Juan Rodríguez Cabrillo (who may be of Spanish or Portuguese nationality) went further north.

On August 5, 1542, Juan Rodríguez Cabrillo reached the Isla de Cedros. On August 13th, he discovered Punta del Mal Abrigo (Punta Canoas). On the 19th, he anchored on San Bernardo Island (San Jerónimo Island) and set sail on the 20th to Punta del Engaño (Punta Baja). On August 24th,

Captain Cabrillo landed and took possession of the port that he named La Posesión (San Quintín) in the name of his Majesty Don Antonio de Mendoza. They repaired their sails, replenished their fresh water supply and discovered salt mines. They also encountered native fishermen and other natives clad in fur and deer skin footwear.

During this expedition, Cabrillo discovered a group of islands on the opposite side of La Mesa de la Cena (known in English as Table Mountain or Mesa Redonda to the Rosarito inhabitants). He called these islands "Islas Desiertas." [b] It was during this journey that Captain Cabrillo's expedition observed very large clouds of smoke along the coast that were produced by the natives to make their presence known. They continued the expedition until they found a new port called "San Miguel," which is now known as Puerto de San Diego. [b]

*Historian assigned to the Institute of Historical Investigations of the Autonomous University of Baja California.

The San Martín Islands

New explorations were conducted after the turn of the 16th century. During Sebastián Vizcaíno's journey (November 9, 1602), two islands and three sea cliffs were discovered at latitude 33°, which he named San Martín. These islands were located about 12 to 15 miles from the coast, outside of a very large bay known today as San Diego Bay. [b]

Along the route from Acapulco to Cabo Mendocino, Gerónimo Martín Palacios recorded a description of the Baja California coast all the way up to Cabo de Todos Santos, which is located at the southern end of the current Bahía de Ensenada, where they arrived on November 5, 1602. From here, he headed north. As he traveled he wrote: "From this point to the isles of San Martin there are ten leagues of 'les sueste ues-norueste' firm land with hidden mountain ranges. Among them, to the northeast of these islands, is a very high plateau, so high that it looks like a pedestal, which is called the supper table. One league to the southeast, there is a hill with two peaks on the sides that resemble the Calvary." [c]

Enrico Martínez drew the maps and charts during this expedition. He noted the leading geographical features described by Gerónimo Martín Palacios (the expedition's cosmographer) as El Calvario, La Mesa de la Cena, the San Martín islands and Puerto Bueno of San Diego. He described the San Martín islands as "four steep, treeless precipices, of which the largest is the one closest to firm land" and as something that could "offer shelter from the west wind." [c]

He continued his journey to the Puerto Bueno de San Diego where he claims there were "plenty of chinchorro fishing using nets and fishing poles, and many natives with bows and arrows, good people willing to trade with the Spanish." [c]   Father Antonio de la Asención came along on this expedition and wrote that at other ports and islands they discovered many natives "who called us through smoke clouds."

They finally "reached the end with much difficulty, arriving at the port of San Diego, which is very good and has much potential and offers many good amenities that make it inviting for the Spaniards to inhabit...since it is a calm port and is inhabited by good natured natives of very friendly demeanor... there are many different fish of very good taste and flavor...the natives walk painted with black and white and dark blue oils." [c]

Father Juan de Torquemada gave another testimony in his Indian Monarchy where he mentions how they reached the inlet they named Todos Santos before continuing north by following the coastline. According to Torquemada it was "wonderful to see all the smoke and fires through which all the natives called the ships. The land seemed good, level and calm. Six leagues from firm land, bordering firm land, are four islands that are called The Coronados Islands; the two small ones are shaped like sugar breads; the other two are

somewhat larger. To the north of these islands, on firm land, there is a famous port called San Diego, where this naval expedition arrived on the eve of San Martín, on the 10th of November, at seven in the evening." [d]

Here the islands are already referred to as Los Coronados, named after the Four Coronados, or Holy Martyrs: Severo, Severiano, Carpóforo and Victorino, martyred in Rome on 302 A.C., and commemorated by the Catholic church on November 8th.

The name of San Martín Islands was registered in the cartography of the time and was seen in subsequent maps created by different authors, like the 1625 map of *America Septentrionalis* by Henry Briggs, or the map by John Overton, printed in London, England in 1668. [e]

The Islands as a Landmark

In 1734, José González Cabrera Bueno's book *Speculative and Practical Navigation* (published in Manila, the Philippines) showed a map course from Manila to the port of Acapulco. He recorded his passing through the port of San Diego and stated

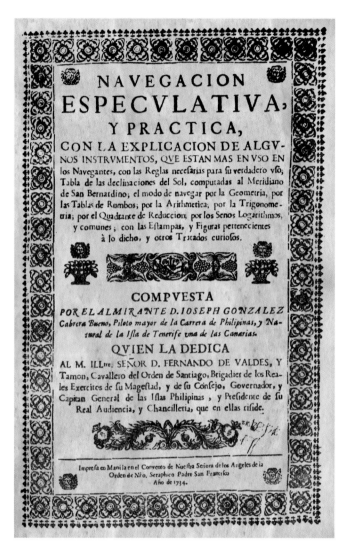

that "about six leagues to the southeast of said port are three small islands with some small sea cliffs laying from the northeast to the south, called the islands of San Martín, which are a very good marker for recognizing the port of San Diego." [f]

Of the many land and sea expeditions that were conducted by 1769, the most important was the one headed by Father Junípero Serra. He had been commissioned to found the missions of Alta California. On May 12, 1769, one of his companions, Father Juan Crespí, wrote in his journal that they had arrived at a ranch on a beautiful plateau resembling an island and that "in front of this place are the four islands called the Four Coronados." They continued their trip until they found "a well populated gentiles' ranch [on] a great plain, that had very good lands all dressed up in very green grass, a beautiful landscape for a mission." He baptized this area Sancti Spiritus, known today as Tijuana. They arrived at the port of San Diego on May 14, 1769, and mentioned the location of the Coronados as being "six leagues in distance from firm land." [g]

Well into the 19th century, a new Spanish expedition was organized with the purpose of surveying the California coasts. Don Gonzalo Lopez de Haro (the person in charge of this mission) was the first pilot to graduate as sub-lieutenant. He was commissioned to "begin a survey of the coast starting at the port of San Diego, and sailing close to land, in order to be able to see clearly any cove, cape, bay, port, river or inlet, for the development of a very detailed map."

Don Gonzalo Lopez de Haro had already made a tour of the Gulf of California aboard the ship "Horcasitas" in 1794, and nine years later, in 1803, was about to navigate it again. He departed from the port of San Blas on April 23rd. He reached Alta California on June 10th at the southern part of the islands in the Santa Barbara Channel. From there he traveled down past Santa Catalina Island and anchored at the port of San Diego on June 15, 1803.

There he inspected the ship and stocked it with water, firewood and food. He set sail on July 3rd and headed south, managing to maintain a steady course along the shore despite the "fog and the lazy winds… that he experienced from the time he left the port." He continued along Cabo San Lucas and entered the Gulf of California on his way north to Loreto.

The Coronados Islands were surveyed and drawn on July 3rd and 4th, taking as reference "the Mesa because of the peak immediately adjacent to it" seven miles from the coast, and setting anchors at the "shelter of the most eastern of the Coronados." July 5th and 6th they headed southward along the coast and saw: on the beach lots of cattle and horses, and a house on a hill, and believed this to be the mission of San Miguel. [Don Gonzalo López de Haro] rushed ahead and hit bottom with the starboard anchor across from a leafy ravine. Shortly after, [Don Gonzalo López de Haro] ordered a cannon to be shot, to see if the house was part of the mission so we could place it on the map. But no natives appeared, neither around the house nor on the beach, so [López de Haro] assumed the place to

be a house used by the priests to store the seeds they gathered from that beautiful ravine.

Finally he arrived to the Port of San Blas on October 31, 1803. It is important to mention that the ship weighed 65 tons and was equipped with two bronze cannons, six iron stone throwers, six guns with bayonets, six pistols and six swords. The food consisted of rations of dry meat, chick-peas and two clay pitchers of oil.

The Islands Appear on the Maps

Guadalupe Victoria (President of Mexico) ordered the drawing of a spherical map with the coasts and gulf of California, called the Sea of Cortés. This map shows the port and military prison of San Diego north of the La Punta Ranch located near the Coronados Islands. This map shows the Coronados Islands by the Sea of Cortés, across from Loreto, northwest of the Isla del Carmen.

A map that included a drawing of the "Plano de San Diego" by Captain John Hall was published in 1839. It is in reference to the military prison of San Diego and also shows the location of the Coronados Islands. [h]

By 1882, the islands were already being explored by scientists. Ornithologist Lyman Belding visited the islands on May 16th and 17th after visiting other places on the peninsula where he made important observations and collected new species of birds. In April 1885, Doctor Edward Lee Greene visited the Coronados Islands from San Diego to conduct botanical research. He continued to the islands of Todos los Santos, Cedros and Guadalupe prior to returning to San Diego in mid-May. In 1889, ornithologist A.W. Anthony collected marine birds. Ornithologists Grinnell and Daggett recorded a description of the islands and wrote down a list of 22 species of birds. [i]

The islands were again visited in June of 1908

by Chester Lamb, who researched the Xantus Murrulet. [j] In the spring of 1909, Pingree I. Osburn observed the island birds. [k] The Coronados Islands have served as a geographic point of reference since the 16th century, since it was the standard landmark used to locate the port of San Diego. During the 18th century they also served as a point of reference to land explorers who reported

seeing the Coronados Islands from Tigre's Slope, north of Ensenada. This indicates their proximity to the San Miguel mission, the Dominican border and the Mission of San Diego of Alcala. The islands also intrigued biologists, divers and tourists who have traveled there from San Diego since the second half of the 19th century.

Works Cited

[a] Martha Micheline Cariño Olvera, History of man-nature relations in South Baja California, 1500-1940, Mexico, Independent University of Baja California Sur (IUABC)/PROMARCO, 1996.

[b] Herbert Eugene Bolton, Spanish exploration in the southwest 1542-1706, New York, Barnes & Noble, Inc., 1963, pp. 18-19.

[b] Ibíd., p. 23.

[b] Ibíd., pp. 3-39.

[b] Diary of Vizcaino in California: Vizcaino expedition, in Bolton, op. Cit. pp. 78-80.

[c] Alvaro del Portillo y Diez de Sollano, Discovery and Explorations in the Coasts of California, Madrid, School of Hispano-American Studies of Seville, 1947, p. 349

[c] Ibíd., p. 401.

[c] Ibíd., p. 349. This document is dated on the Port of Monterrey on the 29th of December of 1602.

[c] Ibíd., p. 425.

[d] Fray Juan de Torquemada, Monarquía Indiana, Edition Miguel Leon-Portilla, Mexico UNAM, 1975, Vol. II, p. 499.

[e] Miguel Leon-Portilla, Cartography and Chronicles of Old California, Mexico, UNAM/ Social Investigations Foundation, A.C., 1989, p. 90.

[d] Ibíd., p. 91. Map of the Hearing of Guadalajara by Nicholas Sanson of 1658, including the Island San Martín.

[f] Jose Bueno González, Navegación Especulativa y Práctica, Introduction and edition W. Michael Mathes, Madrid, Editions Jose Porrúa Turanzas, Collection Chimalistac 31, 1970, p. 337.

[g] Carlos Lazcano Sahagún, Entry 1. Discoveries of the Interior of Old California, Ensenada, Barca Foundation, 2000, p. 286.

[g] Ibíd., p. 287.

[g] Ibíd., pp. 288-289.

[h] Alexander Forbes, California: A History of Upper and Lower California, London, Smith, Elder and Co, 1839.

[i] Edward W. Nelson, Lower California and its Natural Resources, Washington Memoirs of the National Academy of Sciences, vol. XVI, 1921, p. 142.

[i] Ibíd., p. 142. Edward L. Greene, Botany of the Coronados Islands, The West American Scientist, I, No.10, October 1885, pp. 69-71.

[i] Ibíd, p. 163. Grinnell, J. and F. S. Daggett, An Ornithological Visit Los Coronados Islands, Lower California, Auk, XX, January 1903, pp. 27-37.

[j] Chester Lamb, Nesting of the Xantus Murrulet as Observed on Los Coronados Islands, Lower California, The Condor, XI, January 1909, pp. 8-9.

[k] Pingree I. Osburn, Notes on the Birds of Los Coronados Islands, Lower California, Condor, XI, July 1909, pp. 134-138.

1. Archivo General de la Nación, Ramo Historia, vol. 528, exp. 3, foja 62, Copia en el Instituto de Investigaciones Históricas UABC [3.5]

2. *"Carta esférica de las costas y golfo de Californias llamado Mar de Cortés que comprende desde el Cabo Corrientes hasta el Puerto de San Diego construida por los oficiales de la marina española por orden del excelentísimo sr. Don Guadalupe Victoria, Primer Presidente de la República. México Año de 1825."* Colección California Mexicana Ascensión y Miguel León-Portilla del IIH UABC.

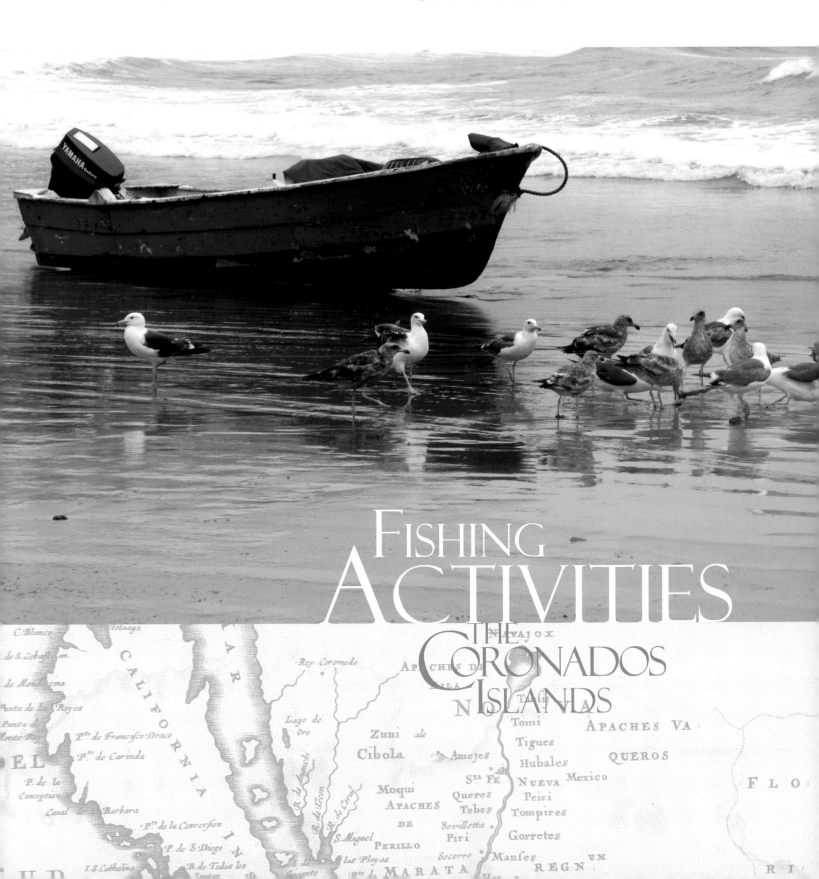

CHAPTER II

FISHING ACTIVITIES

THE CORONADOS ISLANDS

ARTISAN FISHING

CARLOS ISRAEL VÁZQUEZ LEÓN*

Islands are small landmasses with no connections to a continental mass, or bodies of land that separated from continental lands by natural processes. Some were formed by volcanic or tectonic activity. Islands have developed unique characteristics because of their distance and isolation from continental lands.

An island's natural environment is enriched by the nutrients provided by sediments and runoff. Nutrients promote diversification of species that inhabit the islands and their surrounding waters and encourage the reproduction of species sought by fishermen. Some of these species include sargasso (giant algae), sardines, anchovies, tuna, Pacific saury and those that live in rocky or sandy bottoms such as: sea urchin, clams, lobster and abalone.

The Coronados Islands are a group of three islands and an islet located approximately 13 kilometers from Rosarito. The islands have no infrastructure for fishing, fresh water or facilities suitable for human habitation due to the fact that the islands' only residents are a lighthouse keeper and a detachment of the Mexican Navy.

Commercial fishermen benefit from the different local and migrating species found in the waters around the islands. There are several groups of organized fishermen in Popotla and Rosarito who take advantage of the local fish and mollusks. They practice riparian fishing, a type of fishing conducted with panga boats equipped with agallera nets, small dragnets, diving gear and traps.

Currently there are two fishing associations that sponsor some 52 registered fishermen who have permits to fish near the islands, as well as other permitted fishermen who do not belong to the associations. They represent approximately 45 boats, not including the registered lobster fisherman and those who dive for sea urchins and snails.

Fishing Activity

Fishing is a valuable economic resource at the state level. Baja California Norte is the fifth best fish producing state in Mexico. Other fish producing states are Sonora, Sinaloa, Baja California Sur and Veracruz. In 2004, Sonora provided nearly 45 percent of the domestic catch, whereas Baja California supplied about five percent.

Most of Baja California's fishing industry is based in Ensenada, Isla de Cedros and San Felipe. Each specializes in a specific catch. San Felipe's greatest catch is shrimp, the Isla de Cedros are abalone and lobster, and Ensenada's are tuna,

*Studied environmental economy and natural resources with a focus on poverty studies in fishing communities. He is professor-researcher at the Colegio de la Frontera Norte, Urban and Environmental Studies Department. He also teaches environmental economy at El COLEF and sustainable development at Tijuana's Universidad Iberoamericana.

sardines and sea urchin. Canneries and organized fishermen in the Tijuana-Ensenada region specialize in the capture of sea urchin, lobster and scale fish.

Popotla is one of the main fishing ports in this part of the Pacific coast and the one closest to the islands. Popotla's local fishermen have very rudimentary fishing equipment that consists of small panga boats and fishing nets. Their harvests are low in volume and are considered subsistence level harvests. The poor fishing infrastructure and the lack of processing plants and refrigeration facilities for small volume fishing impacts product quality and results in loss of added value.

Most of the regional fish is marketed in Tijuana and Ensenada. Local fishermen have developed informal contracts with restaurant owners who cater to tourists. During the tourist season, restaurants rely on these arrangements to supply them with fresh fish and shellfish.

Another manner of marketing catches is at shore-boat sales. When the pangueros (panga boat fishermen) arrive with their catch of the day, they are approached on the beach by those wishing to buy fresh fish. Shore-boat sales occur predominantly on the weekends since they cater to visitors from Tijuana and Rosarito who seek fresh products at competitive prices.

Since 1995, two groups of organized fishermen have been registered at the port of Popotla. According to fishing statistics, the number of boats and registered fishermen remained relatively stable between 1995 and 2004. In 1997,

records showed only two licensed or private users based out of Popotla who possessed sea cucumber, sea urchin and crab permits.

The fishermen associations are considered unions and provide their members with fishing permits which allow them to claim rights over fishing areas such as the Coronados, where sea urchin and lobster are the main catch.

A fisherman's identity is tied to his fishing area. Most fishermen come from families with a strong fishing tradition, such as the "El Morro" fishermen. They become very attached to the community where they have been fishing for decades.

Fishermen negotiate their fishing permits in the offices of SAGARPA (Department of Agriculture, Cattle Breeding, Rural Development, Fishing and Food) in Ensenada or Mexico City. Fishing permits are valid from one to four years.

Studies are conducted to understand the number of fish that are permitted to be taken. The time frame of the permit and the allowed fishing methods depend on the results of these studies. This information can be found in official publications such as the Diario Oficial de la Federación (Official Newspaper of the Federation). The Carta Nacional Pesquera (National Fishing Chart), first published in 2000, publishes information related to the exploitation levels of the leading commercial species in Mexico.

Commercial fishing near the Coronados Islands is affected by the studies performed by the Instituto Nacional de la Pesca (National Fishing Institute).

The findings are published in the Official Newspaper of the Federation by the Comisión Nacional de la Pesca (National Fisheries Commission).

Sea urchin is one of the species protected by policies based on these scientific findings. The trend of sea urchin fishing is slowing, which probably means they are over-fished. Currently, sea urchin can only be fished by divers using small boats with outboard engines.

Due to the high market-value of lobsters it is difficult for fishermen to obtain lobster permits and rights. Stricter rules and standards and favorable environmental conditions have allowed the take of lobster to increase. Lobster is caught in wire, wood or plastic traps set by 18 to 22 foot panga boats with outboard engines that are generally manned by one or two fishermen.

Sea cucumber is relatively new to the Mexican fishing market, although it is a common product in the Asian markets of Japan and Korea. It has great potential on the Baja California coasts. Divers use panga boats to harvest sea cucumber by hand which is the same method used to catch sea urchin.

Scale fishery is the business of fishing for commercial gain. The coastal region between Tijuana, Ensenada and the Coronados Islands offers a large diversity of fish with commercial value, such as: sardines, anchovies, saury, kelp bass, sole, mackerel and stingray.

Some of these species migrate along the coast, while others are highly territorial and are found in sandy or rocky bottoms. They are captured using wide nets such as trawl lines, gill nets and line nets used on vessels of up to ten metric tons with crews of up to twelve fishermen. They are also used on

panga boats with two to four pangueros. The fishermen work offshore from eight to twelve hours a day depending on the fishing season. The nets are used continuously for ten or eleven months. During the rainy or hightide season the fishermen perform maintenance tasks to clean and repair the meshwork on the nets or trawl lines.

As there is no formal provider of sport-fishing services in the Popotla area, sport-fishing near the Coronados Islands is most frequently provided by vessels registered in the United States. US citizens are able to purchase permits at the San Diego fishing office that can be valid for a day, a week, a month or a whole year. Although sought by commercial fishermen, swordfish is one of the species generally reserved for sport-fishing. There are thirty-four registered boats in Ensenada that possess swordfish permits.

The demand for sport-fishing licenses in Mexico increases from May to September. During summer weekends, up to 400 sport-fishing boats may be found in the Coronados Islands area.

Works Cited
SEMARNAT-CONANP. Previous justificatory study for establishing the protected natural area, Reserve of the Biosphere, "Pacific Islands of Baja California." May 2005Thomson, Cynthya J., Gomez, Santiago I. Results of the Mexican Sport Fish Economic Survey. NOAA Technical Memorandum NMFS Nov. 1992 NOAA-TM-NMFS-SWFSC-173.
SAGARPA. Anuario Estadístico de Pesca 2002. CONAPESCA, México D.F. 2002.
SAGARPA. Carta Nacional Pesquera 2000. CONAPESCA, México, D.F. 2000.

NATURAL RESOURCES

ROBERTO RAMÓN ENRÍQUEZ ANDRADE*

The natural resources generated within insular ecosystems can be of great economic value locally and internationally. They are important for coastal economies because they contribute to the quality of life of the local residents. Such is the case of the Coronados Islands, whose rich natural resources generate services and other economic activities in local, regional and international forums.

Natural capital differs from man-made capital because it is accumulated through natural processes such as the growth-rate of a stock of fish. The optimal use of natural capital, as with any capital, requires a balance between consumption and conservation to ensure the capital's future availability.

Ecosystems are a considerable source of wealth that offer a wide range of economic possibilities. When establishing a resource's total economic value, it is important to identify the economic aspects of that ecosystem and its most profitable long term uses. The total economic value of an ecosystem includes its direct, indirect and passive uses.

The natural resources of the Coronados Islands' ecosystem are common property and it is difficult to limit their access to the many groups that benefit from them. Without regulations, these resources might eventually become degraded or even exhausted. Market forces alone cannot dictate the usage of a natural resource. Interested parties and authorities must collaborate together in the development and enforcement of rules that will protect and maintain these natural resources.

*Research professor at the School of Marine Sciences, Baja California Autonomous University. He has a doctorate in economy of natural resources from Oregon State University, USA. He is a specialist in coastal economy, fishing economy, conservation economy and protected natural areas.

Although there are no exact figures that show the worth generated by the islands, it is possible to estimate their value in relation to comparable coastal ecosystems. A conservative estimate of the total economic worth of a coastal ecosystem (including direct, indirect and passive values) is around $4,000 per hectare per year.[2] This amount, multiplied by the 3,300 hectares comprising the islands and their surrounding area results in an economic potential of $13,200,000 per year.[3] Mexico has not fully taken advantage of this potential. Very few of the economic values associated with the Coronados' ecosystem are acknowledged in market prices. Market failures can be due to the inefficient assignation of common property resources.

Commercial fishing and the cultivation of blue fin tuna are the primary sources of revenue in the waters surrounding the Coronados Islands. Ecotourism however, is a growing industry in Baja California and is rapidly generating the need to provide recreation services for tourists. This form of tourism caters to people who enjoy the natural beauty of birds, geology and marine wildlife. Their activities have little impact on the islands' ecosystem and the revenues provided by ecotourism services feed directly into the local economy. Currently, the leading recreation activities are sport-fishing, diving and wildlife observation/exploration tours.

Unfortunately, Mexico has not made an effort to benefit from these activities. Research shows that sport-fishermen rarely use the Mexican boats located at Playas de Rosarito and Popotla. However, the revenue gained by California-based enterprises from sport-fishing alone reaches to $2.5 million dollars a year. The same applies to sport-diving, wildlife observation tours and scientific research expeditions. Nearly 100 percent of the economic activities in this area are sponsored by businesses, universities or groups based in California.

The United States benefits from these activities in Mexican waters because of their close proximity to the region. Tijuana and Rosarito lack the coastal infrastructure to sustain a thriving ecologically based

economy. Mexico needs to adopt measures to exercise sovereignty over its territorial waters and claim exclusive rights over this lucrative area.

Other Values

Assets such as ecological services associated with habitat, information and regulatory functions are less tangible, but still important. Ecological services must meet two necessary conditions. First, they must arise from the natural environment and be used by people. Second, they must contribute to or improve people's quality of life.

Regulatory functions are the ecosystem's ability to organize ecological processes essential to the existence of life by means of biogeochemical cycles and other biophysical processes. Weather regulation, biological control mechanisms, nutrients control and the mitigation of environmental disturbances are examples of regulatory functions. For instance,

the islands protect the coast from stormy waves. They also play a role in regulating the microclimate and maintaining marine productivity. Another ecological service is water quality maintenance, as it has indirect economic value associated with tuna fattening operations.

Habitat functions are of indirect value because they encourage biodiversity. Economists agree that species diversity contributes to the economic welfare of human beings. There is no substitute for biodiversity because loss of this diversity is irreversible. Habitat functions provide space, substratum and adequate reproduction space to plants and animals. The waters around the Coronados Islands nourish organisms that are later fished in other areas and this increases the capture potential (and profits) for fishing and diving enterprises.

Information services retrieve information from organisms and ecosystems that is of great value in

educational, scientific and technological fields. This type of data is used for scientific research, or to assist activities such as: fishing, aquaculture and agriculture. For example, data regarding the concentration level of certain substances (which was used to reconstruct the planet's geological history) can be found in the genes and hard tissues of organisms.[4] Organisms sensitive to pollution can be useful in monitoring the effect of human activities on coastal waters, while benthic organisms can act as weather and ocean temperature registers.

Option values keep the islands and their ecosystem open to future opportunities, especially since their economic potential (given their proximity to one of the most important world markets) has yet to be determined. One future possibility that could be very profitable is bio-prospecting (search for medicines through nature) for pharmaceutical purposes.[5] A Cartier and Ruitenbeek[7] (1999) study suggests that coral reefs suitable for the development of pharmaceutical products could be worth between $75,500 and $698,000 per hectare.[6]

The legacy value is the part of the islands' resources and ecosystem that the present generation passes on to future generations for their benefit and enjoyment. Fishing resources and the ecosystem's biological potential must be maintained.

Baja Californians value the existence of coastal ecosystems like the Coronados Islands and are willing to invest in them financially to ensure their welfare and survival. The Coronados Islands are a valuable natural asset. Their total economic value should be determined before making decisions that may alter their ecosystem. Institutional reforms would ensure that any economic benefits generated by the islands' ecosystem would remain primarily in Baja California.

Works Cited
1. Hardin, G. 1998. Extensions of "The Tragedy of the Commons." Science, 280: 682-283.
2. Costanza, R., d'Arge, R., de Groot, R. S., Farber, S., Grasso, M., Hannon, B., Limbur, K., Naeem, S., O'Neil, R. V., Paruelo, J.,
   Raskin, R. G., Sutton, P., Van Den Belt, M. 1997. The Value of the World's Ecosystem Services and Natural Capital. Nature, 387(May): 253-260.
3. CONANP (Comisión Nacional de Áreas Naturales Protegidas). 2005. Estudio Previo Justificativo para el Establecimiento del Área Natural Protegida,
   "Reserva de la Biosfera Islas del Pacífico." Secretaría de Medio Ambiente y Recursos Naturales. México, D.F.
4. Moberg, F. y Folke, C. 1999. "Ecological Goods and Services of Coral Reef Ecosystems." Ecological Economics, 29(2): 215-233.
5. Berkes, F. and Folk, C. 1994. Investing in Cultural Capital for Sustainable Use of Natural Capital. En: A.M. Jansson, M. Hammer,
   C. Folke and R. Costanza, (Eds.), Investing in Natural Capital. Island Press: Cocelo, California, pp. 128-149.
6. Fusetani, N. (Ed.). 2000. Drugs from the Sea. Karger, New York.
7. Cartier C.M. y Ruitenbeek H.J. 1999. Review of the biodiversity valuation literature (Chapter 3). En: Ruitenbeek HJ y Cartier CM. Issues in Applied
   Coral Reef Biodiversity Valuation: Results for Montego Bay, Jamaica. World Bank Research Committee Project RPO#682-22, Final Report,
   World Bank, Washington D.C.

FISHING RESOURCES AND AQUACULTURE

JULIO SAID PALLEIRO NAYAR*

The waters adjacent to the Coronados Islands are interesting sites for commercial fishing, sport-fishing and fish farming. It is important to learn about each of these activities in order to fully understand the Coronados Islands.

Commercial Fishing

The most common commercial catch species are primarily benthic species (that live on rocky substratum) such as: the red sea urchin (*Strongylocentrotus franciscanus*), purple sea urchin (*Strongylocentrotus purpuratus*), marine snail (*Lithopoma undosa*), red lobster (*Panulirus interruptus*) and a few fish such as rockfish (*Sebastes spp*), California sea bass (*Paralabrax spp*) and California sheep-head (*Semicossyphus pulcher*). They are caught with nets, lines and traps.

Most commercial fishermen leave from the Popotla docks on 18 to 22 foot boats equipped with 45 to 75 hp outboard motors. They also carry an air compressor and hoses for the divers who work two to three hour shifts at depths ranging from 10 to 30 meters.

The red sea urchin fishery began in 1972 and is primarily

*Researcher at the Instituto Nacional de la Pesca. He is finishing his doctorate in marine ecology at the CICESE. He was head of the fishing office for the state of Baja California from September 1995 to December of 2001.

located close to Ensenada and outside of Santo Tomás and Rosario bays. The capture of the red sea urchin around the Coronados Islands began in the early 1980s. The main areas for catching sea urchin are South Coronados Island and El Bajo, a 20 to 30 meter deep rocky area located south of that island.

In the beginning, sea urchins were cut open aboard ships where their five gonads (reproduction organs) were removed and placed in a bucket. Once on land, the gonads were packed, transported to Los Angeles airport and shipped to Japan, the world's leading consumer of sea urchin.[1] Sea urchin gonads, like caviar, are considered a delicacy in Japan and are usually sold in sushi bars in the form of preserves or paté. The practice of opening the sea urchin onboard the boat ended in 1983, when fishermen were asked to deliver sea urchins intact in order to avoid damaging the gonads. Since 1984, sea urchins caught near the islands have been delivered to Popotla for transportation to processing plants in Ensenada.

Mexican fishermen are paid approximately $25 per kilo of gonads, which requires 15 to 30 sea urchins. The minimum size of capture is 80 mm in diameter.[2] Red sea urchin capture occurs between July and February in coastal Baja California. Since 1990, the sea urchin season has been closed between March 1st and June 30th.

Red lobsters have been captured around the Coronados Islands since the 1970s when SCPP Ensenada (Sociedad Cooperativa de Produccion Pesquera) began operating lobster traps from the US-Mexico border to El Rosario.[3] Some years later the area of operation was reduced and the islands' surrounding area was not assigned to lobster producers until 1996. Currently, two fishermen's organizations possess commercial lobster fishing permits, one of which also has a permit for fish. This organization specializes in the capture of rockfish for sale in California.

The *Macrocystis pyrifera* kelp was harvested from a large boat named El Sargazero around the Coronados Islands until 1993, when these kelp beds

of brown seaweed mysteriously disappeared from islands and Southern California coasts. Possible reasons for its disappearance are strong winter storms, the warming of seawater by the "El Nino" effect, excessive feeding by herbivores such as sea urchin and sedimentation processes.[4] The kelp beds have recently reappeared near South Coronados Island at El Bajo. *Macrocystis pyrifera* communities host large numbers of marine flora and fauna and have a range of diversity that is comparable to the diversity of rain forest species.[5]

Sport-fishing

Sport-fishing around the Coronados Islands occurs primarily on charter boats from San Diego, California. The boats can carry 20 to 50 sport-fishermen for a fee of $70 to $150 per person. Some Mexican fishermen take tourists fishing to the islands from Popotla in small boats with outboard engines. Their rates range from $30 to $40 per person. The main species caught are California sea bass, yellow tail, bonito, kelp bass, sheep-head, rockfish and flatfish or halibut.

The record for the largest fish caught near the Coronados Islands belongs to an American who had been fishing the area unsuccessfully for several years. In 1993, his persistence paid off and he caught a giant sea bass weighing 202 kilos. The fish was so large that the struggling fisherman could not bring it onboard. He had to be helped by another fishing boat captain, who agreed to pull it out and take it to port. Once in San Diego, game wardens from the California Department of Fish and Game were curious as to the fish's origin, since this species of giant sea bass is protected in the state of California. They allowed him to keep his spectacular fish because he had caught it near the islands.

In Mexico, the capture of this species is not forbidden and specimens of this size can be legally caught and kept. This particular specimen may have been 60 to 70 years old (this species reaches maturity at age 11). They are sedentary animals that do not

wander too far from their place of birth.

The March 1977 issue of *Western Outdoors* (a sport-fishing magazine), featured the triangular area between the Coronados Islands, Rosarito and Tijuana for its abundance of flounder and halibut, a fish highly coveted by seafood restaurants. Fishermen have been known to catch flounder weighing up to 12 kilos within this area.

Mexican sport-fishing standards specify that fishermen may keep up to ten fish per day and no more than five of the same species. In the case of marlin, sailfish, swordfish and shark, the limit is one specimen per fisherman per day. One of them can be worth up to five of any other species. Marlin is

sought by sport-fishermen and can often be found in Baja California during El Niño years. During 1997's El Niño, a fisherman caught two marlins that had followed the warm seawater currents moving northward from Los Cabos.

Fish Farming

Fish farming is primarily used to fatten blue-fin tuna (*Thunnus thynnus orientalis*). This technique began in Japan in the early 1970s. By the 1990s, fish farming businesses were established in Australia, the United States, Spain, Croatia, Morocco, Portugal and Mexico. Fish farming began in Baja California in

1997. Currently there are six fish farming companies operating in Baja California. These companies are a source of income and employment for the local Baja California fishermen.

Fish farming was brought to the Coronados Islands in 2001 by an Australian company who set enclosures or floating corrals for the fattening of blue fin tuna. Their boats are used for feeding, safety watches and personnel transportation. Currently there are 18 net enclosures near South Island, each 40 meters in diameter and 15 meters deep.

Blue-fin tuna is captured between May and October, when it migrates from Japan to Baja California in search of food. They are trapped using tuna purse seine nets and are then transferred to transportation nets. The nets are slowly towed to the fattening corrals by a small boat or a tuna fishing boat. Most captured tuna weigh between 20 and 30 kilos. The tuna consume approximately 10 percent of their body weight in fresh or frozen sardines on a daily basis and they are confined for three to five months. Restricted mobility and a steady diet ensure that they gain weight. The fattened tuna are sold primarily to Japanese markets at prices ranging from $17 to $50 per kilo depending on size, quality, supply and demand.[6]

Future Impact

Fishing the waters surrounding the Coronados Islands is an important and lucrative activity that has been well established for over thirty years. Many species thrive in the islands' unpolluted waters. Their conservation by regulations and sustainable fishing practices are instrumental to the continued development of the area's varied fishing industry. Respect for the current fishing regulations will reduce the ecological impact of fishing on the local species and ensure their survival for years to come.

Works Cited

1. Palleiro, J. S. A. Lelevier, M. Navarrete y M. Romero. 1988. Biología del Erizo Rojo S. Franciscanus y su Pesquería en Baja California. Los Recursos Pesqueros del País XXV Aniversario Instituto Nacional de la Pesca, Secretaría de Pesca. p. 661.
2. Palleiro, J.S., D. Aguilar M. y J.M. Romero. 1996. Equinodermos. Erizo de mar. 313-335 pp. Pesquerías Relevantes de México. Instituto Nacional de la Pesca. SEMARNAT. 555 p.
3. Ayala Y, J. G. González y G. Espinosa. 1988. Biología y pesca de langosta en el Pacífico Mexicano. Los Recursos Pesqueros del País. XXV Aniversario Instituto Nacional de la Pesca, Secretaria de Pesca.
4. Dayton, P. K. 1985. Ecology of kelp communities. Ann. Rev. Ecol. Syst. 16: 215-45.
5. North W. J. Review of Macrocystis Biology. 1994. Biology of Economic Algae. Ed. I. Akatsuka Acad. Pub. p. 527.
6. Lozano M. A. y J. G. Vaca. 2004. Ranchos de engorda de atún aleta azul (Thunnus thynnus orientalis) en Baja California: Historia. El Vigía No. 20: 10-12

CHAPTER III

THE PHYSICAL
ENVIRONMENT
THE CORONADOS ISLANDS

GEOLOGICAL HISTORY

JORGE LEDESMA VÁZQUEZ*

The geological origin and history of the Coronados Islands can be explained through a study of its geological components (rocks and minerals) and the processes that act upon them. Tijuana, Playas de Tijuana and the Coronados Islands have very different geological characteristics. The islands have an old and complex history dating back 15 to 30 million years.

The islands are composed of material called blue schist, which originates in deep zones of the continental crust. It is not normally observed because it is generated and transformed at a depth of approximately 30 kilometers and it is usually covered by layers of rock. The presence of blue schist characterizes these rocky islands as a rare sight on the Earth's surface. It is found in only three Baja California sites along the peninsula: the Coronados Islands, Isla de Cedros and Isla Margarita in Southern Baja California.

Younger rocks on the Pacific side of the peninsula date from about 15 million years ago, from the last stages of a volcanic period. During this stage, the region's volcanoes created the rocks found along the coast from Tijuana to Ensenada including those found on the Coronados Islands.

*Professor-researcher of Geology at the Facultad de Ciencias Marinas (UABC). His interest in research includes studies of regional tectonics and sedimentary tectonics associated with extensional inverse basins as well as applied sedimentology.

This geology indicates that the sea level dropped approximately 100 meters, roughly 18 thousand years ago. Because of the lower water levels, the coastline was located farther west of where it is today. The islands came into being when the sea level returned to its current position (which happened more than 5,000 years ago). For many years, dry land connected the islands to Tijuana forming a point, which was an ideal landing site for the settlers reaching North America.

The islands were created in phases. The first phase began 29 million years ago, the second one 15 million years ago, and the last one 18,000 years ago. One method to date geological structures is absolute

dating, a technique that is based on the half-life of radioactive isotopes. These have a constant speed of decay and can provide us with an absolute age as opposed to a relative age, which is when two or more prehistoric phenomena are compared to each other. Given some absolute age data about a structure, the age of its surrounding formations can be estimated. Carbon-14, a radioactive isotope of carbon, was used to determine the age of the archaeological site called Concheros (middens).

The Coronados Islands were once a block, a piece of the crust that was broken off by planes that fracture the rock. These planes or faults move, and cause the blocks to move and generate a displacement. The blocks break off and then they slide.[2] This constitutes the concept of faults. These processes result from the movement of the tectonic plates that cover the earth's surface.

Tectonic plates cover the terrestrial crust like the black and white sections covering a soccer ball. These plates include the continental crust. The deeper layers of the crust are called the lithosphere. It is found at an approximate depth of 60 kilometers (37.28 miles) in continental masses. The islands' lithosphere is found at an average depth of 12 kilometers (7.46 miles).

As the plates move, the solid mass breaks to accommodate the shifting plates. The mass is rigid, and its movements eventually reach the limits of the plate and cause seismic activity and fractures on the earth's surface. Plate fractures are like broken bones. When they break without moving they are called fissures, but when they break off and become displaced, they are called fractures. Geology refers to them as faults when the whole length of the fracture is visible.

When a fault that limits a block shifts from its vertical position and becomes inclined, the rocks that lie above it are also tilted, covering a larger area. These rocks are like a row of domino tiles that have been knocked over. The Coronados Islands are flanked by a pair of this type of fault, a listric fault . They correspond to a period when this region

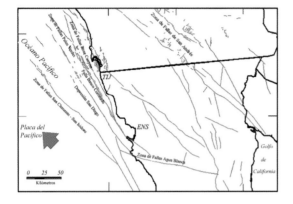

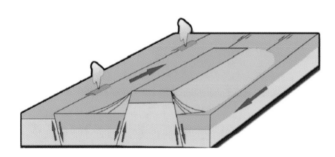

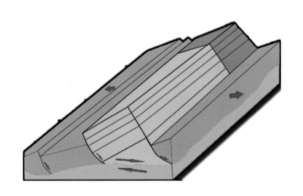

acquired a greater area of continental crust because the original plate that became the islands shifted and widened.[3,4,5] It moved, expanded and rotated .

As a tilted block, the islands have peaks that protrude from the terrain, which makes the islands archeologically significant.[6] Early human settlers preferred to establish their colonies on or near peaks because they allowed them to watch for weather changes and the approach of harmful elements. These high points also accumulated human residue such as food residue, animal remains and marine organisms with shells known as concheros.

When the coastline was several kilometers away from where it is today, the islands resembled Punta Banda, where a rocky mass extends out towards the sea. This provides scientists with a wealth of information for the study of the region's history and evolution.

The Coronados Islands are in a seismic zone. Although tectonic movements occur everyday, most seismic activity can only be perceived by a seismograph. The Earth registers approximately a million earthquakes a year.

The Coronados Islands move an average of five centimeters per year. Some years they do not move at all or they take three to four years to move, but when they do, they move three or four times more than the annual average. Island displacement is now studied with the help of satellites. Scientists use all their resources to identify the changes the islands have experienced throughout the millennia of their existence.

Geology can provide a community with information that is vital to its survival. It can evaluate geological risk factors and propose measures for mitigating such risks.

Works Cited

1.Minch, J.C.,1967. Stratigraphy and Structure of the Tijuana-Rosarito Beach Area, Northwestern Baja California, Mexico, Bull. Geol. Soc. Am., 78, 11551178.

2.Cruz-Castillo, M., 2002, Catálogo de las Fallas Regionales Activas en el Norte de Baja California, México: GEOS, Unión Geofísica Mexicana, v. 22, 1, p. 37-42.

3.Sedlock, R.L., D.H. Hamilton, 1991, Late Cenozoic Tectonic Evolution of Southwestern California, J. Geophys. Res., 96, 2325-2351.

4.Nicholson, C., C.C. Sorlien, T.M. Atwater, J.C. Crowell, B.P. Luyendyk, 1994, Microplate Capture, Rotation of the Western Transverse Ranges, and Initiation of the San Andreas Transform as a Low Angle Fault System, Geology, 22, 491-495.

5.Fletcher, J.M., 2003, Tectonic Restoration of the Baja California Microplate and the Geodynamic Evolution of the Pacific-North American Plate margin, Geol. Soc. Am., Abst. Programs, 35(4), p. 9.

6.Lamb, T. 1978. Geology. In: Kuper H. T (ed.). Natural history of the Coronado Islands, Baja California, Mexico. San Diego Association of Geologists. pp. 12-44.

GEOGRAPHICAL SETTINGS AND CLIMATE CONDITIONS

ENRIQUE NAVA LÓPEZ*

Location and Characteristics

The Coronados Islands consist of three main islands and a smaller islet. They are located in the Pacific Ocean, approximately 13 km (8 miles) off the northwestern coast of Baja California, the northernmost part of Mexico.

South Coronados Island is the largest of the Coronados Islands, with a surface area of 1.460 km² (360 acres). It is 3.48 km (2.16 miles) long and 0.6 km (0.37 miles) wide at its midpoint. The highest elevation recorded is 190 m (623 feet) at the narrow crest that extends along the center of the entire island.

The surface area of the North Coronados Island is 0.471 km² (116.4 acres), measuring 1.45 km (0.90 miles) in length and 0.39 km (0.24 miles) in width, with a maximum elevation of 130 m (426.5 feet) at the central peak of the island.

Middle Coronados Island, also known as Central Coronados or Intermediate Coronados, has a total surface of 0.128 km² (31.6 acres), measuring 0.64 km (0.40 miles) in length and 0.19 km (0.12 miles) in width at its midpoint, with a maximum elevation of 90 m (295.3 feet).

Middle Rock, also called Sugar Mound, is a small islet separated from Middle Coronados Island by a shallow channel. It has a total surface area of approximately 0.042 km² (10.3 acres), being 0.29 km (0.18 miles) long by 0.11 km (0.07 miles) wide, with a maximum elevation of 25 m (82 feet).

*Environmental engineer from the Metropolitan Autonomous University with over 15 years of experience in consulting services and preparing environmental studies. He is manager of the URS Dames & Moore de Mexico Environmental Audits Area.

The islands are masses of steep slopes and craggy peaks that have no valleys, plains or beaches. There are no permanent or temporary sources of fresh water because rainwater quickly drains down the hillsides and slopes or seeps into the rocky surface.

The Coronados Islands are an extrusion of the Mexican North Pacific Continental Platform, which is why they are considered continental islands. The ocean between the islands and the Baja California coast is less than 60 m (196 feet) deep.

Soil Type

There are no scientific soil studies available for the islands to date, but observation reveals shallow and poorly developed soils resulting from the weathering of the underlying rocks. Some areas show white mantles due to the accumulation of guano (sea bird excrement).

The soils of the Coronados Islands are classified by UNESCO (United Nations Educational, Scientific and Cultural Organization) as xerosols and are characterized by arid ocean floors with organic material. The top layer is light colored with a possible sub-accumulation of clay-like minerals and/or salts (such as carbonates and sulfates). These types of soils are found in arid and semi-arid zones and sometimes are associated with regosols (soils with very limited soil development)· These characteristics support different types of vegetation, such as bushes and grasses.[2]

Weather Conditions

The Mediterranean climate in Northwestern Baja California (where the Coronados Islands are located) is characterized by moderate temperatures throughout most of the year and winter rains.[3]

Weather conditions around the Coronados Islands are determined by the presence of cold water from the California Current, alternating low and high-pressure systems and the buffering effect of the ocean surrounding the islands.[4]

The ocean's buffering effect on the Northwestern Baja California coast produces cooler summers and warmer winters than is normal for this latitude. The weather station in Ensenada has recorded an average annual temperature of 17° C. Extreme temperatures (below 0° C and above 32° C) rarely occur in this region.

The winter rains are caused by the southward displacement of the high-pressure subtropical belt. This is a series of high pressure nuclei (fields of atmospheric pressure where the pressure is higher at the center than elsewhere at the same altitude) that occur in both hemispheres.[5] This is why the

prevailing winds are west winds from the Pacific Ocean. They are associated with some disturbances typical of this zone (vortexes, cold whirlpools and cyclonic depressions).[6]

Maximum rain precipitation values on the northwestern coast of Baja California occur from November to March. National Meteorological Service data shows that the mean annual precipitation recorded in this zone is 250 mm.

Fog is a significant component of the weather conditions around the Coronados Islands and it is caused primarily by the California Current, which cools the warmer continental air mass. The fog forms when the relative humidity in the air increases and later cools, causing condensation in the form of water droplets.

No hurricanes have yet reached the Coronados Islands. Out of the nine hurricanes that entered

oceanic-atmospheric system and is characterized by the warming of the surface layers of the Equatorial Pacific Ocean along the coasts of the American Continent from December to March.

El Niño was named by Peruvian fishermen many centuries ago who noticed the change in temperature on the surface of the ocean in December, near Christmas, and associated the event to the arrival of baby Jesus. Though many believe this to be a new development, El Niño is a cyclical event that takes place at intervals of two to seven years and lasts from twelve to eighteen months. The opposite phenomenon of abnormally cold temperature in the Equatorial Pacific Ocean is called La Niña.[8]

One of El Niño's effects on weather conditions is that normally damp regions suffer drought, while normally dry areas experience severe rainfall. These changes impact the availability and quantity of the fish populations that travel along the coastal regions. This subsequently affects the local fishing industry. El Niño may also cause floods, tropical storms, coastal erosion and changes in the food chain of marine species and in coral reefs.

The El Niño phenomenon has undoubtedly impacted the Coronados Islands region. However, there is little scientific data available to confirm the extent of the impact and its potential impact on the currents, temperature conditions and their relationship to surface weather conditions. A current research program which begins at Ensenada and heads south includes sampling in ocean points and continuous monitoring of stations along the Baja California coast. It is directed by the inter-institutional project IMECOCAL (Investigaciones Mexicanas de la Corriente de CaliforniaMexican Research of the California Currents) and it is conducted along the southern section of the California Current. Unfortunately, this project leaves the Coronados Islands zone without direct research.

Baja California peninsula waters between 1949 and 2002, the only one that hit the Baja California state was "Nora" in 1997. "Nora" penetrated approximately 300 km southwest of Playas de Rosarito and had no significant effect on the Coronados Islands region.[7]

However, the Coronados Islands zone is vulnerable to the effects of El Niño. This is a phenomenon caused by alterations to the global

Works Cited

1. Jehl, J.R. 1977. An Annotated List of Birds of Islas Los Coronados, Baja California, and Adjacent Waters. Western Birds 8:91-101.

2. González-Medrano, F. 2003. Las Comunidades Vegetales de México. Propuesta Para la Unificación de la Clasificación y Nomenclatura de la Vegetación de México. INE-SEMARNAT, México. pp. 77.

3. García, E. 1988. Modificaciones al Sistema de Clasificación Climática de Köppen. México. p. 217.

4. Mellink, E. 2002. El Límite Sur de la Región Mediterránea de Baja California, con Base en sus Tetrápodos Endémicos. Acta Zoológica Mexicana (n.s.) 85:11-23.

5. Página Web de la Dirección General de Meteorología. Uruguay. http://www.meteorologia.com.uy/glosario_z.htm (Last consultation: March 17th, 2006).

6. García, E. 1967. Apuntes de Climatología: Según el Programa Vigente en las Carreras de Biólogos de la Facultad de Ciencias, UNAM y de la Escuela Nacional de Ciencias Biológicas del IPN. México. p. 111.

7. Historical Data. Secretaría de Medio Ambiente y Recursos Naturales (SEMARNAT). In www.semarnat.gob.mx/huracanes/en_cifras.shtml. México, 2003. (Last consultation: June 2003).

8. Página Web del fenómeno de "El Niño" y de "La Niña" en el CICESE. http://elnino.cicese.mx/ (Last consultation: March 17th, 2006).

9. IMECOCAL. http://imecocal.cicese.mx/ (Last consultation: March 17, 2006).

10. Badán, D. 1997. La Corriente Costera de Costa Rica en el Pacífico Mexicano. Contribuciones a la Oceanografía Física en México. (3):99-112.

11. Jehl, J.R. 1973. Studies of a Declining Population of Brown Pelicans in Northwestern Baja California. The Condor 75: 69-79.

12. Lamb, T. 1978. Geology. In: Kuper H. T (Ed.). Natural History of the Coronado Islands, Baja California, Mexico. San Diego Association of Geologists. pp. 12-44.

CHAPTER IV

THE ISLANDS AND THEIR HABITAT

THE CORONADOS ISLANDS

VEGETATION AND FLORA

JOSÉ DELGADILLO RODRÍGUEZ*

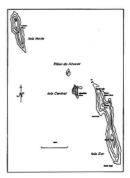

Location of the Coronados Islands
(Taken from Oberbauer 1999).

The Coronados Islands are valued for their ecological, biological and biogeographical characteristics. They form part of the Channel Islands along with the other islands of Baja California and California. These islands include Todos Santos, Guadalupe, Cedros, San Benito, Catalina, Santa Barbara, San Clemente, San Nicolas, Santa Rosa, San Miguel, Santa Cruz and Anacapa.

The descriptions of the flora and vegetation of the Coronados Islands date back to the 19th century. They include the work of J. Bartlett (1854) and Eduard Palmer (1885). In recent years, Thomas Oberbaurer (1986, 1999 a, b) has published several articles related to the flora and vegetation of the Coronados Islands and the Guadalupe and Cedros islands.

Vegetation

The vegetation on the Coronados Islands is classified as coastal scrub. It is representative of the adjacent peninsular coasts, although it is not unique to Baja California.

Coastal scrub includes coastal sage scrub and coastal succulent scrub. Both are present on all four of the islands, although the area of coverage and distribution varies depending on their degree of preservation and alteration. These plants can be found in clumps or as isolated individuals.

Aromatic Coastal Sage Scrub

This plant community is part of the Diegan association and is one of the four Californian coastal scrub associations in California (described by Wesman in 1987). It is found mainly on the northern sides of slopes. It is represented primarily by the

*Professor of botany, Coordinator of the Herbary BCMEX, School of Science, Autonomous University of Baja California.

following species: *Artemisia californica*, *Eriogonum fascuculatim* ssp. *fascicultaum* (alforfón), *Encelia californica* (coastal daisy), *Heteromeles arbutifolia* (Toyon or Christmas berry) and *Aesculus parryi* (pigs' ears). The composite *A. californica*, commonly known in English as sage, is an aromatic plant that is characteristic of Californian coastal sage scrub. However, the genus Salvia (*Lamiaceae*, in the mint and spearmint family), also an aromatic type of coastal scrub generally found in California and Baja California, is not found on the islands.

The structure of the Californian coastal scrub is open and with a shallow root scrub. They are semi woody and can be deciduous (leaf shedding) during droughts, which makes them seasonally dimorphic. The plants grow at least one meter tall, with the A. Parryi and H. Arbutifolia varieties usually reaching a height of up to 2 meters. Their reduced-size organs can be circular or shaped like half moons. Their tendency for compact growth is due to the influence of strong marine winds.

The cliffs of the islands sustain vegetation typical of compact sandstone soils, which include succulent plants such as *Coreopsis maritima*, *Dudleya candida* and *D. Anomala* (evergreens).

Coastal Succulent Scrub

Westman (1981) described this vegetation community as belonging to the Martinian association (characterized by succulent stalks). This group is comprised mainly by cactii species such as *Bergerocactus emoryi* (velvety cactus), *Cylindropuntia prolifera* (cholla), *Opuntia littoralis* (prickly pear) and *Mammillaria dioica*. Other meaty and succulent plants found here are evergreens (*Dudleya attenuata* spp. Orcutti and *Dudleya lanceolda*, of the Crassulaceae family), *Euphorbia misera*, (which includes the "poinsettia") and short scrubs like *Lycium californicum*, *Atriplex canescens*, *Encelia californica*, *Hazardia berberides* and *Rhus integrifolia* (lemonade berry).

Flora

According to Oberbauer (1999), the flora of the Coronados Islands has 39 botanical families and approximately 130 species. All of these are characteristic of the Californian coastal sage and succulent scrub. One hundred of the total species recorded are native to the region and possess certain endemic characteristics. Some are insular: *Eschscholzia ramosa*, *Malacotrix foliosa* and *Malva occidentalis*. For example, *Malva occidentalis* can be

found on Guadalupe Island. Others are exclusive to the Coronados Islands: *Galium coronadoense* and *Malacothrix insularis* on South Island, and *Dudleya candida* on all four islands.

Introduced Flora

The islands sustain approximately 30 species of exotic or non-native plants. They are present in areas where native vegetation has been altered. Most of the islands' non-native plants are of Mediterranean

origin, with the most abundant being *Sonchus*, *Lamarcia aurea* (Brome), *Messembraynthemum crysallinum* (ice plant), *Bromus carinatus* (California Brome), *Malva parviflora* (malva), *Erodium cicutarium* (red-stem stork's bill), *Chenoipodium murale* (lamb's quarters) and *Salsola iberica* (Russian thistle).

Preservation

The excellent preservation status of the islands' flora contrasts dramatically with the poor condition of the coastal vegetation on the mainland, where the natural vegetation has suffered a high degree of alteration. Coastal scrub has decreased 80 percent between the international border north to Arroyo La Mision, where scattered pockets of coastal scrub remain primarily in slopes and gullies.

South Island offers a greater diversity of species compared to the other three islands. However, the long time presence of goats on the island has directly affected the vegetation, specifically Malva occidentals. The goats also indirectly impacted the fauna associated with the vegetation, particularly reptiles, small mammals and birds.

The Coronados Islands are the only Mexican islands in the Pacific with Californian sage and succulent coastal scrub in good condition. The recent elimination of the goat population will allow the damaged areas to recover and the vegetation structure to improve along with the associated fauna.

GEOGRAPHIC LOCATION AND SURFACE

ISLAND	LOCATION (coordinates)	SURFACE	HEIGHT (masl)
Norte	N 32° 28' N W 117° 18'	0.471 km²	153
Pilón de Azúcar	N 32° 25' W 117° 16'	0.042 km²	33
Central o Media	N 32° 25' W 117° 16'	0.128 km²	32
Sur	N 32° 25' W 117° 15'	1.486 km²	220

Works Cited
1. Delgadillo, J. 1998. Florística y Ecología del Norte de Baja California. ed. Universidad Autónoma de Baja California, Mexicali, Baja California. p. 405. Oberbauer, T. 1986. Baja California Pacific Islands Jewels. *Fremontia* 14(1): 3-5.
2. Oberbauer, T. 1999a.Vegetación and Flora of Islas Los Coronados, Baja California, México. Department of Planning and Land Use, County of San Diego.
3. Oberbauer, T. 1999b. Analysis of Vascular Plant Species Diversity of the Pacific Coast Island of Alta and Baja California. Department of Planning and Land Use, County of San Diego.
4. Wallace, G. 1985. Vascular Plants of the Channel Islands of Southern California and Guadalupe Island, Baja California, Mexico. Contributions in Science, Natural History Museum of Los Angeles County. 365: 1-135.
5. Westman, E.W. 1981. Factors Influencing the Distribution of Species of California Coastal Sage Scrub. Ecology 62(2): 439-455.

The South Coronados Island rattlesnake
(Crotalus oreganus caliginis)

REPTILES AND AMPHIBIANS

ROBERT LANGSTROTH*

Considering their reduced geographic space, the Coronados Islands host a great diversity of reptile and amphibian species. There are eight documented species of reptiles and two species of amphibians. Among the reptiles, four are endemic to the islands.[1] With a land surface of 3.61 km², the density is 2.77 species per km. In contrast, Ecuador's famous Galapagos Islands have twenty-three reptile species (no native amphibians) over a surface of 7,635 km², which translates to a density of 0.0029 species per km².

The main explanation for this difference in species abundance is due to the fact that the Coronados Islands are continental islands and the Galapagos are oceanic. Continental islands form part of the continental plate, and platform, while oceanic islands are those typically formed by volcanic action in the open sea. Whereas terrestrial species of oceanic islands arrive by sea (on tree trunks, branches or other floating matter), the Coronados Islands land species probably arrived by land long ago, when dry land still connected the islands to the mainland.

During the glacial phases of the Pleistocene period, the sea level dropped some 120 meters when huge amounts of water became ice layers.[2] Considering that the depths of the seafloor between the Baja California coast and islands are no greater than 30 meters, the lowering of the sea level resulted in an extensive land connection. Reptiles and amphibians thus were able to freely move between the islands and the peninsula for several millennia during the different glacial epochs of the Pleistocene, that is, until about nine thousand years ago.

Amphibians

Amphibians are scaleless animals that usually lay larvae (tadpoles and salamander larvae) that spend their first stage of life in water. These include anurans (frogs and toads), salamanders and caecilians (wormlike amphibians). The only amphibians on the Coronados Islands are salamanders. Baja California anurans cannot breed on the islands because of the lack of fresh water required to lay their eggs and grow their tadpoles. Conversely, the Coronados Islands salamanders

Endemic species are those geographically limited to a specific place (island, state, country, etc.)
The **Pleistocene** is the geological period known as "the ice age" that began 1.8 million years ago and ended approximately 8,000 to 10,000 years before our time.

*Ph.D. in geography and is a specialist in the biogeography of reptiles and amphibians of the Americas. He is manager of the Ecosystems Management Area in the environmental consulting enterprise URS Corporation in Mexico City.

The arboreal salamander
(*Aneides lugubris*)

belong to a group that directly develops its eggs without an aquatic phase.

The arboreal salamander (*Aneides lugubris*)

The arboreal salamander is brown colored with small yellowish spots and can be found on all the islands, although according to Grismer, between 20 and 30 percent of the individuals on North Coronados Island have no spots. Another difference between island and peninsula populations, noted by Grismer, is that the islands arboreal salamander has notably reduced membranes between its digits. It grows to 18 centimeters of which the head and body take up 6 to 10 centimeters.

Although its common name suggests it lives on trees, this salamander is most frequently found under rocks and fallen tree trunks. It preys on invertebrates and even other salamanders, which it bites with great pressure, thanks to its large and muscular head.

In Baja California, the arboreal salamander is found only on the Pacific slope and only as far south as the El Rosario zone. To the north, it reaches

The garden slender salamander
(*Batrachoseps major*)

THE CORONADOS ISLANDS

The California side-blotched lizard
(*Uta stansburiana elegans*)

Northern California and the Sierra Nevada.

The garden slender salamander

(*Batrachoseps major*)

The garden slender salamander has a very long shape, short legs and small head. It is found on all the Coronados Islands as well as on the Isla Todos Santos located near Ensenada. It is found in Southern California and Northern Baja California. Just like the arboreal salamander, its distribution in Baja California extends to the El Rosario zone, only on the Pacific slope. It also inhabits Todos Santos

Island near Ensenada. The species Batrachocheps major consists of a northern and a southern genetic group.

Anny Peralta, of the Baja California Autonomous University, studied the genetics of the Coronados Islands salamander and found that they are almost identical to San Diego's coastal populations and that they differ noticeably from the Baja California and Todos Santos Island samples. The islands' salamanders are the only Mexican population known of the northern group. The other Mexican populations belong to the southern group.

The Coronados skink
(Eumeces skiltonianus interparietalis)

According to Grismer, the Coronados Islands' garden slender salamanders are more robust than those of the peninsula and Isla Todos Santos. Their heads are wider and their tails shorter. The Coronados Islands are important for the garden slender salamanders' diversity in Mexico.

Reptiles

Reptiles have scales, breathe using lungs and lay shelled eggs. They can be ovoviviparous or viviparous.[3] Among reptiles, we can find lizards, snakes, turtles, crocodiles and tuatara lizards (primitive reptiles from New Zealand). Reptiles also include birds, although in common use and tradition, birds and reptiles are considered separately.

Reptiles generally do not require a lot of water to survive and are tolerant of arid conditions. Low temperatures and poor sunlight actually limit the activities of reptiles since many species warm up and gather energy by sunbathing. They also "incubate" their eggs with solar energy.

Lizards

The California side-blotched lizard
(Uta stansburiana elegans)
Side-blotched lizards are found along the Western

The Coronados Islands dwarf alligator lizard
(Elgaria nana)

Viviparous animals have offspring that develop inside the mother and nurture through the placenta. Ovoviviparous lay eggs with membranous shells and are born inside the mother, like rattlesnakes.

THE CORONADOS ISLANDS

The silvery legless lizard
(*Anniella pulchra pulchra*)

United States and Northwestern Mexico. According to Klauber they can be found on the Coronados Islands on sunny days, resting in the sun or hiding between the scrub and the prickly pears, especially in the lower areas of the islands. They can reach a length of 10 to 12 centimeters. Males are territorial and have color markings on their throats.

Coronados Islands tiger whiptail
(*Aspidoscelis tigris vivida*)

Tiger whiptail lizards have very long tails and have bifid tongues similar to serpents. This subspecies, endemic of the Coronados Islands, was identified by James Walker in 1981. He noted that their coloring was more vivid and contrasting than that of continental populations.

Tiger whiptails are heliothermal, meaning they have to warm up in the sun for their body temperatures to reach temperatures higher than that of the air (at least between the temperatures of 37° to 39° C according to Zweifel[2]). Consequently, tiger whiptails are active only when there is sunlight. These hunters seek their prey with their olfactory apparatus and tongue, which constantly inspects chemical stimuli. These very fast lizards use their claws as rakes in search for prey under dead leaves and the ground.

The Coronados Islands skink
(*Eumeces skiltonianus interparietalis*)

The Coronados skink are small lizards with a long body, small legs and long tails. They are covered by smooth and shiny scales. Juveniles have very colorful blue tails. According to Zweifel, the South Coronados Island skinks are common on cloudy days because this species can begin its activities when its body temperature reaches 14° C.[4] Despite its common name, this animal is not endemic to the Coronados Islands. It is found on the Southern California coast, Northwestern Baja California and on Todos Santos Island.

The Coronados Islands dwarf alligator lizard (*Elgaria nana*)

Despite its common Spanish name, this lizard is neither poisonous nor similar to scorpions. It is small and alligator-like, hence its English name alligator lizard. The species endemic to the Coronados Islands is distinguished from its mainland relatives by its small size. On average, the head-body length of island individuals is thirty percent less than those of mainland populations.

The alligator lizard is found on all four of the islands and is usually more active under cloudy conditions. According to Zweifel, the body temperature of active individuals varies between 20.0° and 24.3° C, which is rather low among lizards. This allows the lizard to function during less favorable conditions.

The silvery legless lizard
(*Anniella pulchra pulchra*)

This lizard lacks legs and feet, but is unlike a snake because it has moving eyelids. This little animal is widely spread in Central and Southern California and in Northwestern Baja California. It is not easily spotted because it spends its days under the sandy ground, coming out to the surface at night to seek its prey.

Snakes

The San Diego night snake
(*Hypsiglena torquata klauberi*)

This small snake rarely exceeds 40 centimeters. It is widely spread throughout Southern California and Baja California. It feeds on lizards and salamanders, immobilizing the prey with mild venom. It poses no risk to human beings. This snake has vertical pupils like many other nocturnal animals.

The Coronados Islands gopher snake
(*Pituophis catenifer coronalis*)

This serpent reaches at least 115 centimeters in length and is the longest snake ever documented on the Coronados Islands.[5] It was collected for the first time in 1908, on South Coronados Island and for the

The San Diego night snake (*Hypsiglena torquata klauberi*)

last time in 1933. There is no record of its presence after that date. According to the stomach contents of two of the four known specimens, this snake feeds partly on young birds or chicks, and probably mice and lizards as well.

The South Coronados Islands rattlesnake
(Crotalus oreganus caliginis)
South Coronados Island rattlesnakes are smaller than the continental coast subspecies, Crotalus oreganus helleri. They are probably no longer than 70 centimeters in length (the longest specimen reported by Klauber was 68.3 centimeters long). The sub-specific epithet, caliginis, means *"of the shadows or darkness"* in Latin. This refers to the weather conditions of the islands.

This rattlesnake preys mostly on lizards and occasionally on mice.[6,7] It feeds on the slowest species of lizard, the alligator lizard, and does not appear to hunt the fastest species, the tiger whiptail. It is probable that the tiger whiptail, like other lizard species, can chemically detect the presence of rattlesnakes by means of its well-developed olfactory system.

Reptile and Amphibian Preservation

A global decline in numbers of amphibians has recently been documented. They are considered the most threatened organisms in the Americas.[8] In Mexico, 54 percent of reptiles and amphibians are either endangered or extinct. Fortunately, the species present on the Coronados Islands are not considered endangered. The arboreal salamander is subject to special protection under Mexican Official Standard NOM-059-SEMARNAT-2001 because of its limited distribution throughout Mexico. There is no direct threat to populations on the Coronados Islands. However, warmer and drier weather conditions due to global warming might affect salamanders.

Reptiles have also suffered a large reduction in their numbers and a few have suffered extinction as a result of loss of habitat, invading species and unsustainable uses of the environment.[9] The species on the Coronados Islands are less threatened because they are protected by the laws prohibiting people's unauthorized arrival on the islands and because the islands are very isolated. The legless lizard, alligator lizard, night snake and rattlesnake are subject to special protection under NOM 059-SEMARNAT-2001, given their restricted distribution throughout Mexico. The presence of four reptiles known as endemic to the Coronados Islands, and six species subject to special protection, emphasizes the conservation importance of reptiles and amphibians from these small islands, and its herpetofaunal diversity in Baja California and Mexico.

Works Cited
1. Grismer, L. L. 2002. Amphibians and Reptiles of Baja California, Including its Pacific Islands and the Islands of the Sea of Cortés. University of California Press, Berkeley. p. 413.
2. Zweifel, R.G. 1952. Notes on the Lizards of the Coronado Islands, Baja California, Mexico. Herpetológica 8: 9-11.
3. Klauber L. M. 1928. Sunday, August 19, 1928 in selected journal entries from the 1920s. <http://www.sdnhm.org/history/klauber/1920s.html>November 27, 2005.
4. Brattstrom, B. H. 1965. Body Temperatures of Reptiles. American Midland Naturalist 73:376-422.
5. Klauber, L.M. 1946. The Gopher Snakes of Baja California with Descriptions of a New Subspecies of Pituophis Catenifer. Transactions of the San Diego Society of Natural History 11:1-36.
6. Klauber, L.M. 1949. Some New and Revised Subspecies of Rattlesnakes. Transactions of the San Diego Society of Natural History 11:61-116.
7. Ashton K. G. 2000. Notes on the Island Populations of the Western Rattlesnake, Crotalus viridis. Herpetological Review 31:214-217.
8. Young, B. E., S. N. Stuart, J. S. Chanson, N. A. Cox & T. M. Boucher. 2004. Disappearing Jewels: The Status of New World Amphibians. Nature Serve, Arlington, Virginia.
9. Gibbons, J. W., D. E. Scott, T. J. Ryan , K. A. Buhlmann, T. D. Tuberville, B. S. Metts, J. L. Greene, T. Mills, Y. Leiden, S. Poppy, & C. T. Winne. 2000. The Global Decline of Reptiles, Déjà vu Amphibians. BioScience 50(8):653-666.

Marine Mammals

BRENT STEWART*

The fauna of marine mammals in the Northeastern Pacific includes animals of two orders in the class Mammalia. Whales, dolphins and common porpoises are in the Cetacean order, which is divided into two suborders: Mysticeti (bearded whales) and Odontoceti (toothed whales). Mysticeti are called baleen whales because they have long keratin plates (instead of teeth) that they use to filter plankton and fish. There are 14 species of Mysticeti that are divided into three families: Balaenidae (right whales), Eschrictidae (gray whale) and Balaenopteridae (rorquals). Rorquals are distinguished from the other two families by their distinctive dorsal fin and a series of furrowed grooves on the throat that expand when they gulp water during feeding. The more diverse odontoceti suborder includes ten families with 70 species and 34 genera.

Seals, sea lions, South American fur seals, sea otters and polar bears are found in the order Carnivora, which at one time was divided into two suborders: Pinnipedia and Fissipedia. Although they are not currently considered suborders, the terms pinnipeds and fissipeds are still used. Pinnipeds (comprised of 36 species and 19 genera) are divided into three families: Phocidae (true seals), Otariidae (sea lions and fur seals) and Odobenidae (walruses). The southern sea otter (*Enhydra lutris nereis*) is a fissiped of the Mustelidae family.

The diversity of marine mammals found in waters around the Coronados Islands includes at least 15 species: five mysticetes, seven odontocetes and three pinnipeds. Their diversity on the islands increases during autumn, winter and spring, but diminishes during the summer months.

Residents That Remain All Year Long and Breed On or Near the Islands.

Pacific Harbor Seal (Phocidae; *Phoca vitulina richardii*)
There are small colonies of Pacific harbor seals on Middle and South Coronados Islands. Births take place between February and April; while mating occurs in April and May. The greatest profusion of seals on land takes place during the molting season in summer. Their population decreases during the winter months. The seals feed relatively close to the beaches where they rest and breed. They eat from

*Senior research biologist at Hubbs-Sea World Research Institute in San Diego, California. He obtained his B.S. and Ph.D. in biology from the University of California, Los Angeles (UCLA). He completed a Master in Sciences degree in ecology at San Diego State University, and was awarded a Juris Doctorate in law from Boalt Hall School of Law at the University of California, Berkeley. He has studied marine mammals in all of the world's oceans, participated in research cruises and has conducted studies on marine fauna of the Northwestern Baja California coasts.

macro kelp forests attached to the sea floor located at an average depth of 100 meters. At times, they can dive as deep as 450 meters. Their diet is very diverse, but in Southern California they feed mainly on rockfish, squid and octopus.

California Sea Lion (Otariidae; *Zalophus californianus*)
This species mates on the islands of the Gulf of California and along the California coast from Baja to Northern California. There are two breeding sites on the Coronados Islands: one on Middle Island and the other one on South Island. The greatest numbers of sea lions on land occurs during their mating season in the summer. In autumn and winter

their population decreases on land because only breeding females remain to feed in the areas near the colony. Non-breeding females, juveniles and adult males migrate to the feeding areas in Northern California, Oregon, Washington and British Columbia. Their diet is diverse, but they prey predominantly on mackerel, anchovies, sardines, squid and rockfish. They generally catch their prey at depths of 50 to 100 meters, but on occasion they are known to dive down to 450 or 500 meters.

Bottlenose Dolphin (*Delphinidae; Tursiops gilli*)
Bottlenose dolphins are found around the world in warm and tropical waters. This type of dolphin has two ecotypes, coastal and oceanic. They may be year-

90

round residents, or seasonal visitors. California coastal populations generally remain one to two kilometers off the coast. They inhabit the waters from central California to Ensenada and sometimes travel even farther south. They remain in the area virtually all year.

Temporary Residents Visiting the Area for Short Periods for Reproduction or Feeding Purposes

Northern Elephant Seal (Phocidae; *Mirounga angustirostris*)
Over-hunting nearly exterminated Northern elephant seals by the end of the 19th century. Remarkably, the species grew and expanded at the beginning of the 20th century. Currently, they breed on islands and continental sites from the middle of the western coast of Baja California to Oregon. There is a small colony on the Coronados Islands. Less than two-dozen offspring are born every year

on a beach off the west coast of South Island. Elephant seals spend most of their lives in the sea. They only come out on land during winter to give birth and breed and in spring and summer to molt. Once they leave the shores, they migrate towards the Northern Pacific, the Gulf of Alaska and the Aleutians islands. When feeding, they dive to 250 to 550 meters and have been known to travel to depths of 1,600 meters below sea level. Their diet consists mainly of squid and deep-water fish.

Common Short-beaked and Long-beaked Dolphins (*Delphinidae; Delphinus delphis and D. capensis*)
There are two recognized species of common dolphin in the North Pacific. The long-beaked common dolphin (*D. capensis*) is found mainly in ocean waters. The short-beaked common dolphin (*D. delphis*) generally inhabits coastal waters in large groups of thousands of animals. There is still no

certainty as to which species is found near the Coronados Islands. There are common dolphins both west and east of these islands.

Their presence and dissemination are seasonal. During winter, they stay southeast of the islands. They move north at the end of the winter and in summer and autumn they move south toward open water. Their diets consist of a large variety of mid-depth fish and squid that live approximately 90 meters deep. They generally eat at night, when fish make vertical migrations.

Pacific White-sided Dolphin (Delphinidae; *Lagenorhynchus obliquidens*)
This dolphin is found in temperate waters along the entire North Pacific. It is found east of the Coronados Islands in Baja California's northwestern coastal waters, but their presence and dissemination are highly seasonal. During winter they are found off the northwestern coast of Baja California and during spring and summer they move towards the south and the west. Their diet consists of fish and squid.

Risso's Dolphin (Delphinidae; *Grampus griseus*)
Risso's dolphin is widely spread in all oceans, in temperate and tropical waters. They live in deep water habitats and their distribution varies seasonally on the continental shelf and in submarine canyons. They are mostly seen to the north and east of the Coronados Islands during autumn and winter when

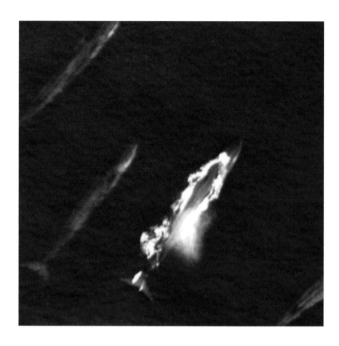

squid (one of their main sources of food) are most abundant because it is their egg-laying season.

Seasonal Migrants Between Reproduction and Feeding Zones

Gray Whale (Eschrictidae; *Eschrictius robustus*)
The gray whale is perhaps the most widely known whale in the American Northwest. It migrates seasonally within the winter reproduction areas of the west coast lagoons that line Baja California and within summer feeding zones of the Bering and Beaufort seas. During both migrations, juveniles and

sexually mature females precede the males. Pregnant females lead the group during the southward migration at the beginning of winter. The mothers and their offspring are the last to leave the lagoons of Baja California. During both migrations, whales pass by the west side of the Coronados Islands. During the southern migration, some females with premature offspring may travel next to the Baja California coast.

Blue Whale (*Balaenopteridae; Balaenoptera musculus*)
Blue whales are the largest animals on earth. They are found throughout the oceans of the world and many migrate among high latitudes (their summer feeding zones) and low latitudes (where they breed and possibly feed). They are temporary residents of the Northwestern Baja California coastal waters, particularly northwest of the Coronados Islands, as they migrate south in early fall and forage in these waters. They primarily eat krill (euphausiids), but when in Baja California waters they may eat pelagic red crab. Their average diving duration ranges from four to seven minutes and can reach depths of more than 200 meters.

Possible Future Inhabitants

Minke Whale (Balaenopteridae; *Balaenoptera acutorostrata*)
Minke whales are widely disseminated from the

Arctic to the tropical waters of the south. They migrate between summer feeding waters and winter reproduction zones and can be seen in continental platform waters and near the coast. Minke whales are uncommon visitors to the waters near the Coronados Islands. They are solitary, relatively small (nearly 10 meters) and their puffs are barely visible. Their diet consists of small fish and krill.

Pilot Whale (Delphinidae; *Globicephala macrorhynchus*)
These whales are found in temperate and tropical waters and occasionally in waters where the continental platform is narrow, or where there are submarine canyons near the shore. They are seasonal visitors to the Baja California northwestern waters. Their presence is related to the concentration of

squid schools, their main source of food. They forage at a depth of 500 to 600 meters.

Orca (Delphinidae; *Orcinus orca*)
Orcas are found in all of the world's oceans. They may be seasonal migrants or a resident population. Some differences have been observed in their feeding behavior depending on their dwelling patterns. Their diet includes fish, squid, sea birds, pinnipeds, whales and dolphins. They are uncommon visitors in Northwestern Baja California waters, where they may prey on gray and fin whales.

Fin Whale (*Balaenopteridae; Balaenoptera physalus*)
Fin whales are widely distributed in all oceans. They may be found in shallow waters near the coast. They feed on fish and can be seen in waters around 180

meters deep. They are uncommon winter visitors to the Coronados Islands.

Dense-beaked and Beaked Whale
(Mesoplontidae and Ziphiidae)
These species are lesser known creatures whose descriptions are based on a few stranded specimens. They are mainly found in ocean waters, especially where the continental shelf ends. They may live either in arctic, temperate, or subtropical waters and feed mainly on squid. The species that might be found in deep waters west of the Coronados Islands are Cuvier's beaked whale, Baird's beaked whale, Hubbs's beaked whale, Blainville's beaked whale and Stejneger's beaked whale.

Humpback Whale (*Balaenopteridae; Megaptera novaenglie*)
Humpback whales are found in Arctic and Antarctic waters as well as in the tropical waters of most oceans. Their distribution is seasonal. They feed at high latitudes in summer and breed in low latitudes in winter. Humpback whales migrate along the coast between Baja California and Alaska. It is possible that the humpback whales found along the southern coast of Baja California and around the Revillagigedo Islands during winter are the same ones that feed off the California coast and perhaps Alaska in the summertime. Their diet is based on krill. Humpbacked whales are uncommon in waters around the Coronados Islands, as they generally travel far from the coast during migration.

Northern Right Whale (*Balaenidae; Balaena glacialis*) Northern Right Whales live in shallow waters near the coast in arctic and sub-arctic habitats, in the temperate waters of the North Pacific. They are rare though at times they have been seen in waters off the west coast of Baja California.

Guadalupe's South American Fur Seal (*Otariidae; Arctopcephalus townsendi*)

The Guadalupe fur seal breeds almost exclusively on Guadalupe Island (the colony's size was estimated at around 7,000 animals in 1994). A small colony was recently established on San Benito del Este Island. Fur seals appear on land in great numbers during the summer breeding season. No fur seals have been seen in the proximity of the Coronados Islands, but they might be migrating over the western side and in the future they may settle on the eastern and southern side of the islands if the population continues to grow.

Southern Sea Otter (*Mustelidae, Enhydra lutris*) Southern sea otters are found in coastal waters of California and Baja California. Currently, there are very few in central California. There is a small population that survived extermination from hunting during the 18th and 19th centuries and has been gradually moved south. They are found in macro kelp forests very near the shores, where they feed on blowfish, abalone, lobster and other mollusks and invertebrates. Occasionally, otters are seen in the northwestern waters of Baja California. They might become more common if the central California population continues to grow and expand southward.

Works Cited

Leatherwood, J.S., Stewart, B. S., and Folkens, P. Cetaceans of the
Channel Islands Marine Sanctuary. Santa Barbara, NOAA, National Marine
Sanctuary Program, Channel Islands, p. 66.

Reeves, R.R. and Stewart, B.S. 2003. Marine Mammals of the World: An
Introduction. Pp.1-64, In: Walker's Mammals of the World. Nowak, R.M.,
Reeves, R.R. and Stewart, B.S. The John Hopkins University Press,
Baltimore, Maryland. p. 264.

Reeves R.R., Stewart, B.S., Clapham P.J., Powell J.A. 2002. National
Audubon Society Guide to Marine Mammals of the World. Alfred A. Knopf,
New York.

Reeves, R.R., Stewart, B.S. , and Leatherwood, S. 1992. The Sierra Club
Handbook of Seals and Sirenians. Sierra Club Books, San Francisco,
California.

SURVIVAL STORIES

MARÍA CONCEPCIÓN GARCÍA AGUILAR*

The islands off the west coast of the Baja California peninsula are the breeding, feeding and rearing sites used by the four pinniped species present in Mexican waters. Pinnipeds are carnivores whose extremities have evolved into fins. They can be observed in the ocean surrounding the islands during their migration. Among these species are the large bearded cetacean (baleen whales or mysticetes) and groups of toothed cetaceans (odontocetes). Some are year-round residents, while others are transient.

The Coronados Islands are visited year after year by hundreds of tourists who come to see the three species of pinnipeds that gather to rest and breed on the islands' rocky shores. Visitors can observe California fur seals, northern sea elephant seals and harbor seals as well as twenty or more species of cetaceans that inhabit the surrounding waters. For most travelers, the sea journey and the visit to the islands presents a unique and fascinating opportunity to view these unique creatures.

This has not always been the case. In earlier centuries, Mexico's Pacific waters and their islands were frequented by other kinds of visitors: furriers and whalers (mainly Russians and North Americans). They hunted sea mammals intensively, dramatically reducing their population and threatening their existence in the Baja California waters.

*Biologist at the Autonomous University of Guadalajara, with a master's degree from the Interdisciplinary Center of Marine Sciences of the National Polytechnic Institute (IPN) and a Ph.D. from CICESE. She has worked on the demography, conservation, and ecological aspects of the behavior of pinnipeds in the Mexican Pacific and the Gulf of California.

Looking at History

The use of sea mammals in Baja California and Southern California dates back several centuries before the arrival of the first European explorers. Archaeological evidence shows that sea mammals were part of the native inhabitants' regular diet all over the peninsula and in California. Remnants of tribal groups' settlements (some of them over 2,000 years old) have been found on some coastal islands.[1,2] Pinnipeds were consumed regularly on the continent and the islands because they are relatively easy to catch while they are resting on the beaches. For instance, sea lions were used for food, clothing and the manufacture of tools over one thousand years before the arrival of European settlers.[3] Cetaceans were also used when their bodies got stranded on the beaches.

Nothing is known about the number of animals captured by the natives of Baja California and California. Recent research on California's San Miguel Island suggests that hunting and other

human disturbance might have been strong enough to modify the pinnipeds' community around the 1460s, which is nearly 80 years before the arrival of the first Europeans.[2] Although there is very little information regarding the history of the occupation of the Coronados Islands, it is certain that they were visited by tribal groups that obtained fish and mollusks for food from the coast, or hunted pinnipeds for food and clothing.[4]

From Use to Exploitation

In 1542, many years after the arrival of Spanish explorer Juan Rodríguez Cabrillo, the use of sea mammals continued exclusively for food and survival purposes. Towards the end of the colonial period, their traditional use was amplified with the beginning of commercial exploitation. Century-old methods for the use of pinnipeds by natives were replaced by the activities of furriers and whalers that hunted from vessels in the Baja California waters.

The first species subject to commercial exploitation were the Guadalupe fur seal and sea otter which were both coveted for their fur. They were abundant along the coast of Southern California and the northwestern coast of Baja California. The full range of the fur seal before this period of exploitation is not yet known, but it is believed that it inhabited several islands located between San Miguel Island and the Revillagigedo archipelago.[5,6] The range of the sea otter extended over the entire American northwest coast, from Alaska to Baja California, possibly around some Mexican islands.[7] A few years later, during the first decades of the 19th century, northern sea elephant seal hunting began on California's islands and soon extended to the islands of Baja California. Their distribution prior to 1840 is unknown, although there are records of animals captured between 1840 and 1846 on Santa Barbara Island, Cedros Island, Guadalupe Island and the Coronados Islands.

The effects of hunting on the populations of the Guadalupe fur seal and the northern sea elephant

seal was evident a few decades after those activities began. By 1820, the colonies of fur seals in Southern California had disappeared; but hunting continued on Mexican islands until 1897, when the species was declared extinct.[8] In the 1850s, sea elephant seals were scarce and in 1870, they were declared extinct.[9] The hunting for sea otter continued until the 20th century. In 1914, the numbers of otters all along the U.S. coast was estimated at less than 50 individuals and currently are not present in Mexican waters.[7]

During the second half of the 19th century, the hunting of whales for economic gains was evident. Whale exploitation in the U.S. began around 1854 with the operation of two stations in California and continued until 1870.[10] During the first period, the gray whale was the primary target, but occasionally, whalers caught other species of mysticeti. Information about this period is very scarce, making it difficult to estimate the number of whales caught before 1900. Since the identities of the whalers that operated in this region are unknown, it is difficult to evaluate their actual impact on the whale populations.

Commercial exploitation of the California fur seal began after 1850. Historic documents regarding the California fur seal reveal that this species received little attention during the first half of the 19th century, although some stories mention that some animals were caught for "preservation activities" during Guadalupe fur seal and sea otter hunting. A change took place during the second half of the 19th century when the technique of organized capture began. It reached its pinnacle in the Baja California islands between 1860 and 1888.[3]

With the availability of modern equipment in the early 20th century, cetacean capture diversified: whalers caught humpbacked whales, common and northern rorqual whales, sperm whales, gray whales and blue whales.[10,11] There is limited information about captures in Mexico's Pacific waters, but it is known that whalers operated in Baja California in winter during the breeding and rearing seasons. The

schooner Carolyn Frances sailed from Mexican to Canadian waters following the gray and humpbacked whales' migration routes. Total whale capture in Baja California waters is unknown, but the fact that between the years 1919 and 1925 more than 900 humpbacked whales were caught gives an idea of the intensity with which they were hunted.[10]

During the whale exploitation period, whale populations in California and Washington decreased dramatically while remaining constant in Baja California. Some researchers have concluded that individuals migrated to these waters either from colonies that were not being exploited, or from zones of lesser impact. The capture of cetaceans continued throughout the Northern Pacific for several decades and many populations were severely reduced. For example, by 1960 more than 23,000 humpbacked whales had been captured in the Northern Pacific. By the end of 1965 their population had been reduced to around 1,000 individuals.[11]

Sea lion hunting was halted around California islands in 1909, but continued in Mexico until 1947. Traditionally, sea lions were captured for their grease, but toward the end of their exploitation their meat was used for the production of dog food.[3] Once the hunting season ended, sea lions were still taken alive from Mexican islands for aquatic shows and as exhibition animals for zoos. Towards the end of the 20th century, all kinds of seal uses and products were forbidden. This was the end of Mexican sea mammal exploitation.

Conservation and Recovery

The consequences of the non-regulated exploitation of sea mammals were detectable within a few years. By the end of the 19th century, two species of pinnipeds, the Guadalupe fur seal and the northern elephant seal, were considered extinct. By the beginning of the 20th century, the sea otter was eradicated from Mexican waters. Fortunately, fur

seal and elephant seals found safe refuge far from the coast on Guadalupe Island. The elephant seal was rediscovered in 1911, and a few years later another group was found in San Benito. In 1925, these mammals colonized San Miguel, Coronados, Santa Barbara, San Nicolas, Año Nuevo, Natividad and San Martin islands.[9] Despite the drastic decrease in population, the elephant seal has currently repopulated the entire region. Today, elephant seals have an estimated population of about 170,000 individuals. This is an excellent example of natural recovery, perhaps one of the most spectacular examples in wildlife.

The recovery of the Guadalupe fur seal has not been as successful. Some were sighted in 1954,[5] yet they remained confined to Guadalupe Island for several decades. Then, in 1997, a colony was discovered in San Benito,[13] and the rate of population growth observed to date offers hope for this species. Although the sea otter is considered

extinct in Mexican waters, their actual status is currently unknown. The only available information is in the form of reports obtained from fishermen who have reported sightings on some Baja California islands.

The hunting of these species ended not because conservation measures were adopted, but because exploitation was so intense that they considered the animals extinct, or no longer economically profitable. However, the case of the mysticete species is different. In 1946, the International Whaling Commission was established to promote the conservation of cetacean populations and regulate the activities of the whaling industry. As part of the effort for the conservation of colonies, the IWC banned the capture of several mysticete species in the Northern Pacific.[11] For example, in 1966, blue whale hunting was banned, in 1971 northern baleen whale hunting was banned and in 1976, fin whale hunting was

banned. Increases in the populations have been observed, as all these species can be seen throughout the regions where whalers used to navigate.

The experience of an uncontrolled exploitation that seriously threatened our natural resources illustrates that although we can benefit from our resources, we must handle them in a responsible manner. Currently, all hunting of marine mammals is strictly forbidden, but other threats to their existence have arisen. Processes that cause habitat destruction, sea pollution and the introduction of exotic species to the islands may endanger the viability and stability of this complex and fragile ecological system. Our society's challenge is to prevent these new threats to natural resources. Our commitment will ensure the survival of these amazing giants of the sea.

Works Cited

1. Poyatos de Paz, G. & H. Fujita. 1998. Equilibrio Entre el Hombre y la Naturaleza: los Indígenas Costeros de El Médano, Baja California Sur. Revista Española de Antropología Americana 28: 11-38.

2. Walker, P. L., D. J. Kennet, T. L. Jones & R. DeLong. 1999. Archeological Investigations at the Point Bennett Pinnipeds Rookery on San Miguel Island. Pp: 628-632. Proceeding of the Fifth California Island Symposium. March 29-April 1, 1999.

3. Zavala-González, A. & E. Mellink. 2000. Historical Exploitation of the California Sea Lion, Zalophus californianus, in Mexico. Marine Fisheries Review 62: 35-40.

4. SEMARNAT. 2005. Estudio Técnico Justificativo para el Establecimiento del Área Natural Protegida "Reserva de la Biosfera Islas del Pacífico de Baja California." p. 175.

5. Hubbs, C. L. 1956. Back from Oblivion, Guadalupe Fur Seal: Still a Living Species. Pacific Discovery 9: 14-21.

6. King, J. 1983. Seals of the World. Cornell University Press. p. 240.

7. Carretta, J. V., K. A. Forney, M. Muto, J. Barlow, J. Baker & M. Lowry. 2003. Draft U. S. Pacific Marine Mammals Stock Assessments: 2003. NOAA-TM-NMFS-SWFSC Tech. Memo. p. 314.

8. Wegeforth, H.M. 1928. The Guadalupe Fur Seal (Arctocephalus townsendi). Zoonooz 3: 4-9.

9. Stewart, B. S., Yochem, P. K., Huber, H. R., DeLong, R. L. , Jameson, R. J., Sydeman, W. J., Allen, S. G. and Le Boeuf, B. J. 1994. History and Present Status of the Northern Elephant Seals Population. In: B.J. Le Boeuf y R.M. Laws (Eds.). Elephant Seals: Population Ecology, Behavior and Physiology. University of California Press, Los Angeles, CA. pp. 29-48.

10. Greg, E. J., L. Nichol, J. K. B. Ford, G. Ellis & A. W. Trites. 2000. Migration and Population Structure of Northeastern Pacific Whales Off Coastal British Columbia: an Analysis of Commercial Whaling Records from 1908-1967. Marine Mammals Science 16: 699-727.

11. Perry, S. L., D. P. DeMaster & G. K. Silber. 1999. The Great Whales: History and Status of Six Species Listed as Endangered Under the U.S. Endangered Species Act of 1973. Special Issue, Mar. Fish. Rev. p. 74.

12. Maravilla, O. & M. Lowry. 1999. Incipient Breeding Colony of Guadalupe Fur Seals at Isla San Benito del Este, Baja California, México. Marine Mammals Science 15. pp. 239-241.

Land Mammals

*ROBERTO MARTÍNEZ-GALLARDO,
*RICARDO GONZÁLEZ GÓMEZ,
*ALDO GUEVARA CARRIZALES.

Mexico hosts approximately 500 species of wild mammals. There are 140 that are native to Mexico. Many of them only exist on 63 of the 326 Mexican islands. They include seven orders of land mammals. Studies have found 23 families, 59 genuses, 120 species and 124 subspecies on Mexican islands. The islands with the greatest diversity of land mammal species are: Cozumel (Quintana Roo), which has 32 varieties, San Jose (Southern Baja California) and María Cleofas (Nayarit) that have 12 each.

The Coronados Islands have not been studied extensively despite their proximity to the major city of Tijuana. Only two recorded mammal species are considered native to the islands: the mouse (Peromyscus maniculatus assimilis) and the rabbit (Sylvilagus audubonii confinis).

*Ph.D. in biology from the UNAM. He is dedicated to the study of wild mammals and to the management and conservation of the regional wildlife. He is professor-researcher at Baja California Autonomous University.

*Biologist from the UAM Iztapalapa. He is devoted to the study of wild fauna. He is currently a technician at Baja California Autonomous University.

*Biologist from the Technological Institute of Ciudad Victoria, Tamaulipas. He is devoted to the study of wild fauna. He is currently working on his Master's Degree in Management of Arid Zone Ecosystems at Baja California Autonomous University.

Description and Natural History of Land Mammals

Field Mouse (*Peromyscus maniculatus assimilis*)
The field mouse is native to the islands as a subspecies, although as a species it is widely disseminated throughout North America.

It is mid-sized and can be brown, gray or dark cinnamon in color. It has large, prominent eyes and ears. Its tail is bi-colored, with dark dorsal markings. It has a white or light-colored ventral section and chest. They measure about 178 mm in length, with a tail about 80 mm long. It ranges in weight from 10 to 32 grams.

This mouse inhabits rocky areas and semi-desert regions sparsely vegetated by cacti. It feeds mainly on seeds, succulent plants and insects. The species is found on the flat and rocky areas of the islands.

Desert Cottontail Rabbit (*Sylvilagus audubonii*)
The desert cottontail rabbit is a brown rabbit with a white abdomen and a bright copper band on the back of its neck. It mates twice a year and produces anywhere from one to six young per mating. It feeds on scrub, some cacti and mesquite. This solitary animal rests during the daylight hours and is most active at dawn and dusk. It inhabits desert and grassland scrub from California to Texas and throughout Northwestern Mexico.[1]

According to Huey,[3] the subspecies *Sylvilagus audubonii sanctidiegi* is native to Baja California. It is found on the Coronados Islands and within the area around the US/Mexico border, the Arroyo El Rosario basin, the Pacific coast and the base of the Baja California Mountains.

Some reports state that the subspecies found on the Coronados Islands is *Sylvilagus audubonii confinis*, which is normally found south of the Arroyo El Rosario basin. As it would be practically impossible for these animals to reach the islands on

their own, it is much more likely that the subspecies found in the islands is in fact *Sylvilagus audubonii sanctidiegi*.

Are There Any More?

Additional studies and monitoring would facilitate the documentation of other native species of land mammals on the islands and detect whether species from the peninsula use the islands seasonally. Bats, for example, are a species that might be present on the islands. Bats are capable of spreading their populations over large areas. They feed primarily on insects. Considering the short distance between the peninsula and the islands, it would be easy for mainland bats to seek food and refuge there.

Works Cited

1. Chapman, J.A. 1999. Desert Cottontail (Sylvilagus audubonii). In: Don E. Wilson and Sue Ruff (Eds.). "The Smithsonian Book of North American Mammals." The Smithsonian Institution. pp. 624-625.
2. Couoh, R. 2005. Estado de Conservación de la Quiropterofauna en el Matorral Rosetófilo Costero de Baja California, México. Master Thesis, Management of Arid Zones' Ecosystems. Department of Science, Universidad Autónoma de Baja California. p. 72.
3. Huey, L.M. 1963. "The Mammals of Baja California, Mexico," San Diego Society of Natural History, Vol. 13. pp. 87-165.
4. López-Forment, W. C.; I. E. Lira y C. Müdespacher. 1996. Mamíferos: Su Biodiversidad en las Islas Mexicanas. A.G.T. Editor, S.A. México, D.F. 182 pp.
5. Martínez, R. 2003. Mamíferos Terrestres del Matorral Rosetófilo Costero de Baja California. Bight Bulletin 6: 8-11.

SEABIRDS

EDUARDO PALACIOS*

Seabirds are perhaps the most prominent and familiar residents on the coasts and islands of Baja California. People enjoy seeing them on the beaches and at sea, where they often guide fishermen to a bountiful catch. They contribute to the local economy by attracting bird watchers and tourists. Most seabirds nest on the islands because they provide predator-free nesting sites and an abundance of food. Predators and food availability are the factors that naturally regulate the islands' sea bird populations. Habitat alteration, human disturbances and the introduction of wild mammals are the main factors that threaten the populations of the birds.

Ecological Services of Seabirds

One of the most important ecological services provided by seabirds is that they recycle nutrients that limit phytoplankton growth. Seabirds fertilize the sea with their guano which is rich in nitrogen and phosphorous. The guano increases the primary productivity of the ocean. They also clean organic waste materials along the coast and in the sea.

Seabirds are good indicators of marine ecosystem health as they are very sensitive to natural and man-made environmental changes. Birds have been used as models for the progress of ecology for many years. On some desert islands, sea bird colonies maintain the food chain by importing energy from the water. When adult birds bring fish to feed their offspring, the remains of those fish also feed and sustain invertebrate scavenger populations, which in turn serve as prey to other predators. This establishes a complete food-chain cycle that otherwise would not exist on islands with little or no vegetation.

*Ph. D. from the University of California, Davis. He is a researcher at the Scientific Research and Higher Learning Center (CICESE) in Ensenada, B.C. He has studied marine birds in Northwest Mexico since 1985, with emphasis in species with conservation problems. He has also coordinated several nature conservation projects for conservationist civil organizations such as Pronatura, A.C. and Pro Esteros.

Seabirds

At least 5,000 seabirds belonging to twelve species breed on the Coronados Islands. Seven of these species are diurnal and five others are nocturnal. Diurnal species include the brown pelican, three species of cormorants (see Table 1), the black oystercatcher, the western gull and recently a colony of the brown booby. All but the black oystercatcher nest in colonies located on the slopes and cliffs of the Coronados Islands. Nocturnal birds nest in burrows and caves on the Coronados Islands. These birds include three species of petrels (Table 1), Xantus's Murrelet and Cassin's auklet. They visit their nests only at night and are rarely seen from land. They come out at night to feed or congregate in the waters adjacent to the islands.

The Coronados Islands host the world's largest known population of Xantus's Murrelet and a large number of the ashy storm-petrel. The Coronados Islands have the only nesting colonies in Mexico, as well as one of the two breeding populations of Leach's storm-petrel in Mexico.

Sea Bird	Status in Mexico	No. of Birds
Leach's storm-petrel	Threatened	>200
Ashy storm-petrel	Threatened	4-6
Black storm-petrel	Threatened	>500
Brown booby		7
California brown pelican		1400
Double-crested cormorant		600
Brandt's cormorant		100
Pelagic cormorant		6
Western gull		1,000
Black oystercatcher		20
Xantus' Murrelet	Endangered	1500-2500
Cassin' auklet	Threatened	Unknown

Table:
Status of seabirds breeding
on the Coronados Islands.

The species with the largest populations on the Coronados Islands are the brown pelican and Xantus's Murrelet. The biology of these two species shows the range of breeding strategies among seabirds. Pelicans are large, diurnal birds that raise their chicks in or near a nest. Conversely, the Xantus's Murrelet is small and nocturnal with chicks that leave the nest upon hatching to develop at sea far from the islands.

Brown Pelican

Spring is probably the best time to visit the Coronados Islands. From afar, the islands seem devoid of fauna and vegetation, but upon approaching them, hundreds of fluttering western gulls can be heard emitting their noisy squawks. Hundreds of pelicans establish their nests on the highest peaks and quietly lay in them incubating their eggs or protecting their recently hatched chicks.

Apart from the western gulls, the brown pelican is perhaps the most prominent and popular of all seabirds nesting on the Coronados Islands. It is known for its large size, long beak and enormous gular pouch. Of the seven pelican species in the world, the brown pelican is the only marine bird with dark feathers. It is also the only pelican species that uses a diving technique when they feed. When fishing, its gular sack expands to a capacity of over 10 liters and catches fish by using its beak like a dip net. Later it tilts its head on its chest to drain the water and swallow the fish. The four toes in each of its feet are joined by a membrane, making them powerful swimmers, but clumsy walkers.

The mating and breeding process of pelicans starts earlier than that of western gulls. Male pelicans arrive on the island first and establish a territory that they defend from other males. The small territory must be attractive to the female and adequate for building a nest and rearing chicks. The male begins the courting process by displaying different mating dances, as well as head, neck and wing movements. It bows and moves its head and neck from side to side, motioning a horizontal figure-eight. Its gular pouch turns a deep purple red, sending females the signal that it is ready to mate. The male must be sufficiently aggressive to keep other males at bay, but not so much so as to discourage the female.

As the female responds to the male's invitation, it acquires the same deep color in her gular pouch and enters the territory chosen by the male. The male selects the nesting site and the female gets to select

both the male and the nesting spot for breeding. Once the couple is established, the male copulates with the female and immediately begins to gather materials necessary for the construction of the nest. The female is in charge of building the nest with the materials brought by the male from other parts of the island. Generally, a female produces two to three white eggs, which both the male and the female incubate for a thirty-day period. Both sexes also feed the chicks. Unlike other birds, pelicans lack a nesting patch or featherless zone on their abdomen and must incubate their eggs under the membranes of their feet. During the incubation period, one of the parents stays in the nest while the other one keeps watch and makes feeding trips.

New hatchlings are grayish blue and featherless and need adult protection to regulate their body temperature. Adults feed small chicks with pre-digested fish that they regurgitate in the nest. Chicks are large enough to swallow full-sized fish when they are three to four weeks old. They feed by inserting their beaks into their parents' throats, which forces them to regurgitate. Young pelicans mainly feed on small pelagic fish such as sardines and anchovies. Each chick consumes up to 400 grams of fish per day. Chicks are capable of flying and being on their own at 11 to 12 weeks of age, but do not reach sexual maturity until they are three to five years old.

When food is scarce (with the invasion of tropical warm waters or El Niño), pelicans abandon their nests, eggs and chicks, which starve to death or become meals for gulls or crows. This gradual abandonment occurs when the adults (unable to find food in nearby waters) are forced to go further and further away from the nest until they are incapable of returning. When the remaining mate is not relieved, it too ends up abandoning the nest to look for food. Like most marine birds, pelicans have long lives (up to 43 years) and can let a season go by without breeding because they know they will have other opportunities.

Xantus's Murrelet

The Xantus's Murrelet is a small black and white nocturnal marine bird about 24 centimeters long. It only nests on islands from Southern California to central Baja California. There are only 5,000 to 12,000 Xantus's Murrelets of breeding age in the world. The Coronados Islands are especially important to this species as they are the location of one of the largest populations of this bird.

Murrelets are not seen during the day, but as soon as night falls, their screech and whistle noises can be heard. Their nesting period extends from mid-March to early July. The female lays one or two eggs of varied colors. Each egg weighs approximately 22 percent of an adult's weight, making them the heaviest eggs in proportion to the weight of all adult birds.

Unlike other nocturnal species of marine birds (like petrels), the Xantus's Murrelet does not burrow in the ground. They usually excavate a small hole in the ground that serves as their nest. If the ground is too hard, the eggs are laid directly on the ground, in crevices, in cliffs, under large protruding rocks or in dark corners of caves. On other islands, they can nest under dense shrub, which is scarce on the Coronados Islands.

The nest's proximity to the water varies. Some nests are found a few meters away from the ocean, while others may be on a high peak several hundred meters from shore. Couples tend to remain together and return to the same nesting site year after year. Both males and females develop a pair of incubation patches on both sides of their abdomens. Both participate in the nesting and each remains over their eggs for a period of three days. After five weeks of

incubation, the chicks hatch and spend only one or two days in the nest before leaving the islands with their parents.

Vocalization between parents and chicks plays an important role in escorting the chicks toward open seas, where the chicks develop under their parents' care. Xantus's Murrelets feed on fish larvae and crustaceans and work in pairs. This occurs between mating seasons.

The main predators of Xantus's Murrelet are the peregrine falcon and the owl, which also nest on the islands. Rattlesnakes and western gulls prey on the chicks while rats and mice (both introduced by man) seek the eggs. Feral cats (introduced to the islands) are the most aggressive predators of this species. They are capable of exterminating an entire Murrelet colony, which has already happened on other Baja California islands.

Management and Conservation

Seabirds depend on the Coronados Islands for survival. In recent years, many efforts have been made to protect the sea bird colonies and other natural resources found on these islands. The most important step in the preservation of the islands is the eradication or control of introduced predators. Efforts are being made to eradicate the cats and rats that threaten nocturnal marine birds. Efforts are also being made to rid the islands of goats and donkeys because they destroy the natural habitat.

The success of bird preservation programs is dependent on public interest, public understanding of bird biology and on focusing political thrust. Tourism can be of great assistance in conserving the islands' natural resources, but tourist visits must be very carefully controlled. Disturbances caused by visitors may result in the abandonment of marine bird colonies, like the pelican colony on South Coronados Island.

Works Cited

1. Drost, C. A., and Lewis, D. B. 1995. Xantus's Murrelet (Synthliboramphus hypoleucus). In The Birds of North America, No. 164 (A. Poole and F. Gill, Eds.). The Academy of Natural Sciences, Philadelphia, and The American Ornithologists' Union, Washington, D.C.
2. Gress, F., Palacios, E., Harvey, A.L., Alfaro, L., González, E. and Anderson, D.W. 2004. Seabird Status in the Mexican Portion of the Southern California Bight. Unpublished report. California Institute of Environmental Studies, Davis, CA. (prepared for U.S. Geological Survey). p. 26.
3. Lamb, C. 1909. Nesting of the Xantus Murrelet as Observed on Los Coronados Islands, Lower California. The Condor 11: 8-9.
4. Shields, M. 2002. Brown Pelican (Pelecanus occidentalis). In The Birds of North America, No. 609 (A. Poole and F. Gill, Eds.). The Birds of North America, Inc., Philadelphia, PA.

CHAPTER V

THE MARINE ENVIRONMENT

THE CORONADOS ISLANDS

OCEAN IN MOTION

LUIS GUSTAVO ÁLVAREZ*

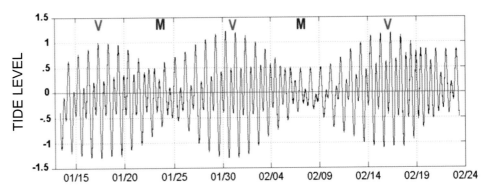

Figure 1. MID-TIDE LEVEL IN FRONT OF ROSARITO DURING 40 DAYS
(January 14- February 23, 1999). Spring Tides (V) and Neap Tides (M).
The height is relative to the average sea level, indicated by the red line.

Tides

Tides are the result of the force between the sun, moon and the earth, which cause the ocean's surface to rise in a long and continuously traveling wave. Tides travel from south to north along Baja California. The high tide shows first in Ensenada, Mexico and about 15 minutes later in La Jolla, California, located 130 kilometers north. Tides around the Coronados Islands are similar to those of Ensenada and La Jolla.

Most tides are semi-diurnal because the two "high tide-low tide" cycles take place in one day. Figure 1 shows the tides in Rosarito, Baja California over a 40-day period. Here, a two-week cycle is observed in which there are high-range tides (the large vertical distance between the high tide and the low tide levels) called spring tides and others of smaller range, called neap tides. Spring tides are observed around full and new moon days and neap tides take place during the first and third moon quarters.

The mean sea level is obtained by averaging the hourly measurements of the sea level at a particular site during several years. Important tide levels related to the mean sea level have been defined. They are useful for designing projects along the coast and for drawing depth charts for navigation safety. In Ensenada, the mean high tide level is 0.781 meters above mean sea level, while in La Jolla, California, it is 0.791 meters. In Ensenada, the mean low tide level is 0.822 meters below mean sea level and in La Jolla, California, it is 0.833 meters below mean sea level. These levels are almost identical, with barely a

*Oceanographer who graduated from the UABC. He holds a masters of science degree in oceanography from Oregon State University and a Ph.D. from the University of Wales, United Kingdom. He has been professor-researcher at the School of Marine Sciences and is currently a CICESE researcher in coastal oceanography and sediment dynamics.

centimeter difference between the two locations. The maximum difference between ebb tide and high tide levels observed in Ensenada is almost 2.9 meters.[1,2]

Waves can also cause rapid changes in the sea levels and strong winds can force the water against the coast creating high elevations called storm surges or wind surges. In January 1988, a powerful storm produced winds that caused an increase in sea level that ranged from 20 to 25 centimeters in Ensenada and La Jolla.[3]

Tsunamis (waves created by earthquakes and fast sea bed displacements) are another factor that may cause the sea level to change at a particular time and place. The effect of a tsunami varies according to the characteristics of the ocean floor and the shape of the coastline. The tsunami generated off the coast of Alaska in March 1964, caused a 0.6-meter wave in La Jolla, California, which is located on an open coast. However, in Ensenada (located within the Todos Santos Bay), the tsunami wave was amplified and raised the sea level almost 1.5 meters above the tide level. It was very fortunate that the tsunami wave arrived during the low tide.[1,2]

Waves

Waves that reach the Coronados Islands are mainly formed by winds in two specific regions: the North Pacific Ocean and the waters off Baja California.

Figure 2. The photograph shows distant ocean waves from the southwest and local ocean waves from the northeast coast of Rosarito, B.C. The bars in the wave diagram indicate the frequency and direction of their origin. The colors indicate the wave's height distribution. (Photo: INEGI)

When strong winds from the North Pacific persist for several days with little change in direction, they generate large swells typical of winter wave climates. These are long-period waves, meaning that the time between the passing of one wave and the next is relatively long (generally between 12 and 16 seconds). The local winds off the Baja California coast generate the waves more frequently observed during the year. The locally generated waves have shorter periods (less than 10 seconds) and are not as regular as those generated from larger distances.

Local waves generally travel in the same direction as the wind that causes them. Distant swell, however, approaches the coast according to the location of the storm that generated it and the shape of the ocean floor near the coast. The photos in Figure 2 illustrate these two types of waves in Rosarito.

The height of a wave is measured from its lowest part (the trough) to its highest (the crest). The wave height is indicative of the amount of energy a wave will transmit to the coast and to the structures standing in its path. The relationship between the height of a wave and the energy it generates is such that a three-meter wave generates nine times more energy than a one-meter wave. Since the height of waves varies markedly, it is the average height that is used as a useful reference. What is often reported is

the significant height or the average height of the top third (or 33 percent) of all observed waves.

A statistical study shows that along the Rosarito coast, almost 80 percent of the waves arrive from the west and southwest. Nearly 52 percent of the waves have a significant height of less than one meter. Less than one percent of the wave heights range from three to six and a half meters. Wave heights on the eastern side of the South Coronados Island are smaller (less than two meters) because the island forms its own barrier against waves coming from open seas, especially from the west (see diagram in figure 2).[5]

Currents

The California Current flows south from Canada to Baja California. It flows almost parallel to the coast, carrying cold water in a southwest direction from Southern Canada down to the tip of the Baja California peninsula. It is part of a great oceanic swirl that covers the entire width of the North Pacific between the coasts of North America and Asia. At the Coronados Islands latitude (32° 25' N), the California Current is approximately 700 kilometers wide and 150 meters deep.[6]

The Coronados Islands are located 12 to 15 kilometers offshore, on a shallow platform less than 50 meters deep on the southern end of the Southern California Bight (which extends about 400 kilometers from Point Conception in California to the U.S./Mexico border). Inside this bay, the main current runs north and northwest (in the opposite direction of the offshore California Current).

The islands region represents a very small area within the California Current system. Coastal

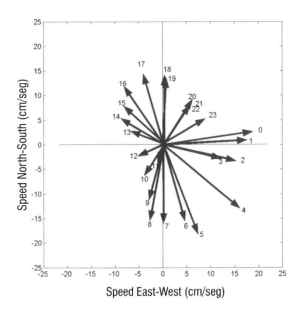

FIGURE 3. Mid currents near the ocean floor, to the east of the Coronados Islands during 24 hours. The arrows indicate the direction and speed-current, the numbers indicate the hour of day. The fastest current was 20 cm/seg. at 4 am. This variation of speed is typical of the wave currents.

irregularities, such as capes and bays, increase the current's complexity and cause it to fluctuate in speed and direction.

The weather, including seasonal weather conditions, can also affect noticeable changes in speed and direction from one site to the next. Inter-annual changes caused by phenomena such as El Niño have been observed to occur every three to seven years. There are shorter, sporadic changes along the coast, where wind changes affect the surface current between day and night.[8] Tides also produce currents that vary throughout the day (Figure 3).

The current system is so complex that new characteristics are still being discovered after almost a century of studies, especially in the local currents of small regions. Currents can behave differently in places barely a few kilometers apart along the coast.[9] It is impossible to accurately describe the currents around the Coronados Islands based on

Noticeable events of mid-currents at 24 meters below sea surface, at 4 kilometers northeast of Coronados Islands.

Date, 1987	Flow Direction	Typical speed in cm/sec
February 23-28	northbound	10-15
March 10-16	southbound	15
March 21-26	southbound	10
May 18-31	southbound	20
June 22-27	northbound	10-15
July 5-9	northbound	10-15

observations obtained at another locality, even if this locality is only a few kilometers away.

Studies of the currents around the Coronados Islands began in 1985 with observations performed during short periods of time (weeks). The current speed and direction was measured at different levels between the surface and ocean floor. Two traditional methods were used to obtain these measurements: fixed current meters (set at four and ten kilometers offshore and at 15 and 24 meters below the sea surface) and buoys floating adrift to record the current's path at the surface and at mid depth.[10]

The results show variable currents, with speeds ranging between seven and 35 centimeters per second. The direction was similar on the surface and near the bottom even though the surface current was up to two times faster than that at depths greater than fifteen meters. This is not unusual because the current is slowed down by the friction with the ocean floor.

It was observed that the current flow was almost parallel to the coast, but it changed direction for several days heading south (usually deemed normal) and later shifted north for several days. This contradicts the expectation that the current will always run southward, like the California Current. These frequent changes in the current flow were verified in 1987 and are listed in the following table.

The study of different paths of currents is useful in estimating the destination of objects or substances moving with the water such as plankton, nutrients, and sediments, including pollutants. This technique allows us to track the movements and travel time, sites of arrival, as well as seawater renovation capacity.

Figure 4 shows the current trajectories between the Coronados Islands and the coast during southbound surface currents. The speed at which the buoys separate from each other while moving with the current provides the information needed to calculate the ocean's dispersion capacity at that particular spot, meaning its ability to dilute substances mixed with water, or to spread objects or particles in the sea. The dispersion capacity is a combination of the turbulent motions formed by small swirls about the size of the spill, acting jointly with the current's transporting capability.

Practical Applications

The study of local currents can help predict the movement of materials released into the water depending on the winds and the average surface currents. In autumn, surface offshore waters would move southeast towards the coast and would travel 20 nautical miles per day. Conversely, in summer,

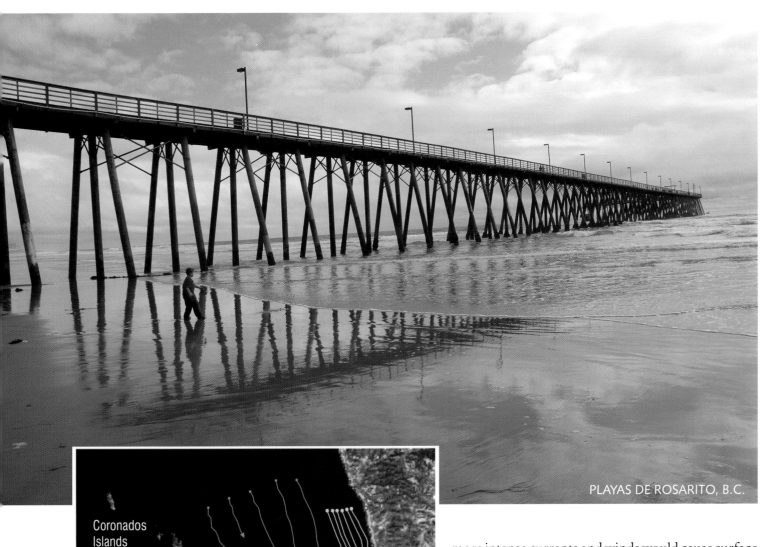

PLAYAS DE ROSARITO, B.C.

Coronados
Islands

5 km

Rosarito

Figure 4. Current trajectories from the south at sea surface during June 1986. The longest trajectory was 9 km in 7 hours. (Average speed of 36 cm/seg.)

more intense currents and winds would cause surface waters to travel 40 nautical miles per day.[11] This data illustrates how long a surface water patch would take to reach the mainland from the Coronados Islands (approximately a quarter of a day in summer and half a day in the fall).

Other similar problems can be solved by calculating the displacement and dilution of a water patch based on the currents and turbulent mixing (rough water). Current conditions can be measured using the paths of surface buoys (Figure 5). Through similar experiments, diffusion coefficients were obtained to estimate the turbulent mixing. Using this information and a mathematical dispersion model, the spreading of the water patch, its dimension and dilution were calculated at different distances and times.[12, 13] This example is based on observations made in coastal waters from Tijuana to Rosarito. Preliminary calculations need to be improved by implementing more extensive observation programs and using better computational tools. Currently, more accurate studies are being performed using new technology that combines satellites, coastal networks for remote observation and mathematical models.

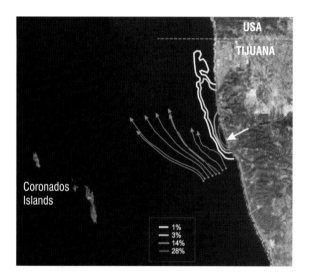

Figure 5. Theoretical extension of continuous residual water drained to the beach during one day (white arrow). The mixture of conditions and the northern current (blue arrows) were observed during July of 1985. The colored lines represent the percentages of dilution in regards to the maximum concentration.

THE CORONADOS ISLANDS

Works Cited

1 Estudio Geográfico de la Región de Ensenada, B.C. Dir. Gen. Oceanografía y Señalamiento Marítimo. Secretaría de Marina. México, D.F. 1974, p. 465.

2 University of California. http://scilib.ucsd.edu/sio/tide/

3 Flick, R. E. & Badan-Dangon A. 1989. Coastal Sea Levels During the January 1988 Storm Off the Californias. Shore and Beach, October, 1989.

4 CICESE. http://oceanografia.cicese.mx/predmar/

5 Sandwell. 2003. GBS Environmental Conditions Summary.

6 Sverdrup, H.U., Johnson, M.W. and Flemming, R.H. 1942. The Oceans, the Physics, Chemistry and General Biology. Prentice Hall Inc. p. 1087.

7 Jones, J.H. 1971. General Circulation and Water Characteristics in the Southern California Bight. SCCWRP Report, October 1971, p. 37.

8 Parés Sierra A., López M. and Pavía E. G. 1997. Oceanografía Física del Océano Pacífico Nororiental. En: Lavín M.F. (Ed.) Contribuciones a la Oceanografía Física en México. Monografía No. 3, Unión Geofísica Mexicana, pp. 1-24.

9 Winant, C.D. 1983. Longshore Coherence of Currents in the Southern California Shelf During the Summer. Jour. Phys. Ocean., vol 13, pp. 54-64.

10 Álvarez, L.G., Godínez, V.M. and Bravo, A. 1989. Trayectorias de Corrientes y Ejes de Difusión Frente a la Costa de Tijuana, B.C. (1985-1986). Informe Técnico OC-89-03 CICESE, Ensenada, B.C., p.113.

11 Adamo, L. C. and Love, C. M. 1974. Seasonal Mean Transport of Hypothetical Oil Slicks in Southern California Waters. Intersea Research Corporation. Unpub. Rep.

12 Álvarez, L.G., Godínez, V.M. and Lavín, M.F. 1990. Dispersión en la Franja Costera de Tijuana, Baja California. Ciencias Marinas, 16 (4), pp. 87-109.

13 Godínez Sandoval V. M. 1986. Dispersión Frente a la Costa de Rosarito. Tesis de Licenciatura, U.A.B.C., Ensenada, B.C., p. 69.

THE CURRENTS

REGINALDO DURAZO ARVIZU*

Over the past few decades we have witnessed a large increase in the number of human settlements along the coast in Mexico and the United States. This has led to an increase in the volume of human and industrial waste being dumped directly into the sea, which has a significant impact on water quality. Recent studies of sediment deposited in California's waters show a decrease in the levels of a lead derivative after 1970 due to the decreased usage of that metal in California.[1] However, the levels have increased in Baja California waters due to a boost in industrial activity.

In the region between San Diego (California), Rosarito and the Coronados Islands, seawater flows freely between Mexico and the United States carrying suspended materials such as larvae, nutrients, pollutants and plankton. The marine ecosystem surrounding the Coronados Islands can be modified by events taking place elsewhere. Currents can affect the distribution, abundance and settlement of marine species of larvae. Populations of abalone, lobster, sea urchins and marine organisms in larval state are transported by currents and settle on rocks or kelp beds around the islands. The quantity of these organisms affects the distribution and abundance of the marine kelp that supplies their food.

*Oceanographer from the School of Marine Sciences (FCM) of the Baja California Autonomous University (UABC).
He obtained his master's degree in physical oceanography at the Center of Scientific Research and Higher Education of
Ensenada (CISESE), as well as a Ph.D. from the University of Wales, United Kingdom. He had post-doctorate work from
the Naval Graduate School of Monterey, California. He is currently a full time professor-researcher at the UABC- FCM.
His interests are coastal circulation and hydrography studies.

Given the increase in human settlements and the industrial developments that they generate, environmental studies would help people to better understand and support the Coronados Islands Natural Protected Area. It is necessary to measure the currents to determine the patterns of material transportation in the Coronados Islands region. During the 1980s, several institutions pioneered studies on currents and dispersion patterns between the Tijuana-Rosarito coast and the islands with the purpose of attaining this goal.

The coastal region south of the US/Mexico border is now considered a potential site for energy-related developments. This attempt to reaffirm and extend progress to Northwestern Mexico has attracted national and international attention. Mexican and American researchers continue to conduct observations of coastal water activity that

Figure 1

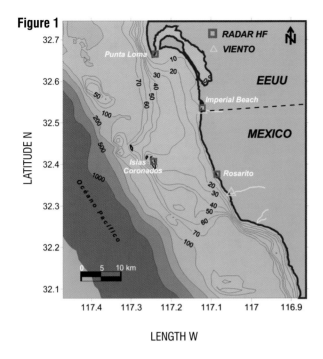

Regional Ocean Currents

Red squares indicate the location where CODAR stations are located. Yellow triangles show the locations where meteorological parameters are measured. Contour lines on the sea provide sea floor depths in meters.

started in October 2002. This coastal observation project relies on a set of radars known as CODAR (Coastal Ocean Dynamic Application Radar).

CODAR stations provide maps of surface currents from the coast to approximately 30 kilometers offshore. They are posted every hour. The observatory has four coastal stations, two in the U.S., (Point Loma and Imperial Beach) and two in Mexico (Rosarito and South Coronados Island). Routine meteorological observations are also conducted in the area.

Figure 1 shows the site map and indicates the location of the CODAR stations. Each CODAR station transmits low frequency radio waves that travel over the surface of the ocean and records the reflected signal to measure the current. All records are kept in a database that is available to the general public. This is the first time these types of studies have been conducted at a national level. They have resulted in the establishment of a Coastal Environment Oceanographic Observatory (a prototype of the environmental oceanic monitoring program that is expected to be implemented in other regions of the country).

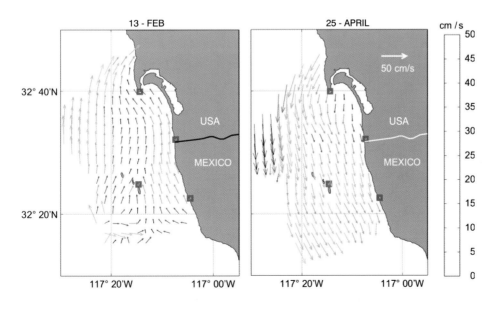

Figure 2

Average Surface Currents Maps for February 13 and April 25, 2003

The size and color of each arrow show the intensity of ocean current. Red squares indicate the location on the coast where CODAR radars are recording. Black arrows show that the current is greater than 50 cm/s, over the maximum of the color scale on the right side.

Figure 2 shows an example of surface current fields obtained using CODAR. The maps present the average currents recorded during a period of 24 hours on February 13, 2003 and April 25, 2003. The arrows show the direction of the current. The size and color of the arrows show the intensity of the current. Two contrasting scenarios are shown in this figure: one with northbound water flow (February 13) and the other with southbound flow (April 25). On February 13, current flows along the coast and are more intense (between 30 and 40 centimeters) in the western region. A 30 centimeter current is approximately equivalent to a displacement of slightly less than 30 kilometers per day. On April 25, the water flows south, with intense currents (black arrows) further offshore. In both cases, any suspended material will be carried by these currents in the direction shown.

These maps illustrate the capabilities of the instruments used, as well as the resources available for studying the transportation of materials. Observations recorded since 2002 show a considerable variation in surface currents, mainly in response to the forces of natural agents such as wind and tides. Changes in current direction and intensity have been observed within a few hours. Currents forming swirls or whirlpools may occur. Likewise, the current may change rapidly in response to dominant winds, especially in response to extreme events (such as storms) originating in the northwest

during the winter and in the southwest and east when there are Santa Ana winds.

Institutions participating in this oceanographic observation are still analyzing the information collected to establish average patterns of coastal circulation. They are also studying the relevance of changes in physical processes on currents and the transportation of materials through the region.

Although the maps shown previously represent the average surface current for those days, the database includes the surface current maps for each hour since October 2002. Current maps are available online at http://sdcoos.ucsd.edu. Maps of currents can provide information necessary to mitigate the effects of pollution.

Information about the marine currents around the Coronados Islands explains the dispersion patterns of plankton and fish larvae of commercial interest. These studies identify the rate of larva settlement required to successfully reach their adult phase. The knowledge obtained through these procedures allows for the appropriate handling of resources and the development of preservation provisions. It provides for better management of this marine environment used and valued by the millions of people that inhabit and visit the area.

MARINE PHYTOPLANCTON AND TROPHIC WEB

*RUBÉN LARA LARA
*CARMEN BAZÁN GUZMÁN

A variety of organisms, from microscopic bacteria to huge whales, thrive in the waters that cover seventy percent of our planet's surface. Victor Hensen first used the word "plankton" at the end of the 19th century to identify a new group of marine life. Plankton consists of an infinite variety of microscopic plants and animals that move through the oceans carried by marine currents.[1]

The definition of plankton is very broad, so it has been classified into more specific categories based on different criteria. Phytoplankton is capable of synthesizing its own food. Like most plants, it absorbs hydrogen and oxygen from water, carbon from carbon dioxide (gas) and luminous energy through photosynthesis.

Phytoplankton and Food Production

Ninety-five percent of living marine organisms owe their existence to phytoplankton, the base of the food pyramid for all marine ecosystems. It consists primarily of microscopic unicellular algae. It is different from zooplankton, a heterotrophic organism that is unable to synthesize its own food and must obtain it from external sources by ingesting living or dead particles.[2]

*CICESE researcher since 1976. He is a specialist on photosynthesis and carbon cycles in the ocean. Currently, he is studying carbon sources and sinks off Mexico's Pacific coast to understand future climate conditions, as well as the environmental and socioeconomic impact caused by global climate change.

*Research technician at CICESE. She collaborates with the research group on marine phytoplankton. She is a specialist in field experiments, and laboratory analyses of variables and processes related with the marine carbon cycle.

Phytoplankton and Climate Changes

Phytoplankton is the leading force behind the biological pump that is responsible for extracting carbon from the atmosphere and transporting it to the deep sea (photosynthesis and extraction). It is one of the most important processes in global research. This process reduces the accumulation of carbon dioxide in the atmosphere, which in turn reduces the greenhouse effect and global climate changes.

Global climate change is a challenge facing today's society because of its environmental and socio-economic impact on the world's ecosystems. Marine phytoplankton plays an essential role in future climate conditions. Understanding their role will allow us to create and implement adaptation and mitigation strategies that will reduce the impact of climate change.[3]

Main Groups of the Phytoplankton

The main groups of phytoplankton are prokaryotic, blue-green algae (Cyanophyta), flagellated and dinoflagellates (Pyrrophycophyta), siliceous algae, diatom, brown algae, "coccolithophorids" (Chrysophyta) and green algae (Cyanophyta).

Many blue-green algae absorb nitrogen, which is very important because nitrogen is a limiting nutrient in the ocean.

Species of Phytoplankton

Phytoplankton is the agent by which solar energy is introduced into marine ecosystems and is the basis for their preservation. It produces organic matter that will later be of benefit at all trophic levels.

Coastal areas (such as the Coronados Islands) have significant water movement due to surf, tides and currents. They experience deep surges of cold

water that contains enough composite nutrients (nitrogen and phosphorus) to classify them as productive zones.

Trophic Chains

The organic material produced by phytoplankton is consumed by herbivores which serve as prey to carnivores in the first link of the trophic chain. Carnivores in the second link and so on may in turn consume these. Zooplankton are consumer organisms that need to obtain their food from other organisms. Those who feed directly on vegetation are called primary consumers and herbivores. Those that obtain their food from other animals are called secondary consumers and are referred to as carnivores. Within this group of plankton organisms, some are capable of feeding on either food source. Some filter phytoplankton indiscriminately and some selectively capture animal organisms (omnivorous).

As we move up the chain, zooplankton is consumed by small fish such as sardines and other such animals called tertiary consumers. Larger fish,

THE CORONADOS ISLANDS

or quaternary consumers, consume these before they are finally caught and consumed by man.

Feeding aspects are complex and intertwined, which is why the term "food chain" has been replaced by food web or trophic web. These terms express a more accurate description of the complicated food interrelations that take place in the ocean.

Organisms can be producers or consumers based on how energy flows through an ecosystem. Consumers (*heterotrophs*) obtain their energy from carbon bonds originated by the producers. The

trophic levels identify an organism's position within the web. Autotrophs are at the bottom of this chain.[2]

The waters around the Coronados Islands are part of the California Current, which begins above latitude 40° N and represents the extent of the Aleutians Current. The California Current is very complex and has its own warm-temperate and subtropical biota. It is influenced by the North Pacific Current (the route of the Central Pacific anticyclone) and to a lesser extent, the equatorial water mass.[5]

The pattern of seasonal abundance of phytoplankton in California Current waters generally shows minimum values in the winter and an increase in the spring. It may continue without change or with a slight increase through the summer months and finally drop in value in autumn, thus completing the annual cycle. Spatial and seasonal variability can be very important. Natural phenomena (such as *El Niño* and *La Niña*) affect the plankton's structure, abundance and consequently affecting the entire trophic web. Although their seasonal abundance and variability is unknown, the waters surrounding the Coronados Islands hold a similar concentration of phytoplankton.

Works Cited

1. Parsons, T., M. Takahashi. 1973. Biological Oceanographic Processes. Pergamon Press. p. 186.

2. Raymont, J.E.G. 1983. Plankton and Productivity in the Oceans. Vol. 2 . Zooplankton. Pergamon Press. p. 824.

3. Fasham, J.R. 2003. Ocean Biogeochemistry: The Role of the Ocean Carbon Cycle in Global Change. Springer-Verlag. p. 297.

4. Larkum, A., S. Douglas y J. Raven. 2003. Photosynthesis in Algae. Kluwer Academia Pub. p. 477.

5. Sverdrup, H.U. M.W. Johnsos y R.H. Fleming. 1942. The Oceans: Their Physics, Chemistry and General Biology.
   New Jersey: Prentice-Hall. p. 1087.

THE CORONADOS ISLANDS

Their History and Environment

Their History and Environment

THE CORONADOS ISLANDS